Brief Atlas of the Human Body

Gary A. Thibodeau, PhD
Chancellor Emeritus and Professor Emeritus of Biology
University of Wisconsin—River Falls
River Falls, Wisconsin

Kevin T. Patton, PhD
Professor of Life Sciences
St. Charles Community College
Cottleville, Missouri

Adjunct Assistant Professor of Physiology
St. Louis University Medical School
St. Louis, Missouri

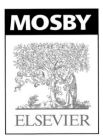

MOSBY

ELSEVIER

i

MOSBY
ELSEVIER

11830 Westline Industrial Drive
St. Louis, Missouri 63146

BRIEF ATLAS OF THE HUMAN BODY FOR ANATOMY AND PHYSIOLOGY

Notice

Knowledge and best practice in this field are constantly changing. As new research and experience broaden our knowledge, changes in practice, treatment and drug therapy may become necessary or appropriate. Readers are advised to check the most current information provided (i) on procedures featured or (ii) by the manufacturer of each product to be administered, to verify the recommended dose or formula, the method and duration of administration, and contraindications. It is the responsibility of the practitioner, relying on their own experience and knowledge of the patient, to make diagnoses, to determine dosages and the best treatment for each individual patient, and to take all appropriate safety precautions. To the fullest extent of the law, neither the Publisher nor the Authors assumes any liability for any injury and/or damage to persons or property arising out or related to any use of the material contained in this book.

The Publisher

ISBN/Part Number: 9996024571

Executive Editor: Thomas J. Wilhelm
Managing Editor: Jeff Downing
Associate Developmental Editor: Jennifer Stoces
Editorial Assistant: Carlie Bliss
Publishing Services Manager: Deborah L. Vogel
Senior Project Manager: Steve Ramay
Design Manager: Mark Oberkrom

Printed in the United States of America

Last digit is the print number: 9 8 7 6 5 4 3 2 1

Contents

Introduction to the Brief Atlas of the Human Body

During our many years of teaching anatomy and physiology, we have found that supplemental images of body structures often help students appreciate the "big picture" of human anatomy and physiology. For that reason, we wanted to provide some of these images in a handy supplement to *Anatomy & Physiology (6th edition)* to help you with your learning.

This *Brief Atlas* contains images from some of the world's best medical atlases. It provides a manageable overview of the human body in an easy-to-use size and format. You will find it helpful for learning in both the lecture/discussion part of the course and in the laboratory part of your anatomy and physiology course.

Part 1 *Surface Anatomy* provides a brief overview of the surface structures of the body. Notice that these images feature the locations of major structures that lie just under the skin. These underlying structures include bones, muscles, and various other internal organs. These images will help you understand the relationship of the internal organs to the surface view of the body.

Part 2 *The Skeleton* features a number of detailed photographs of the human skeleton. These images include many views of the skull from a variety of different perspectives, both internal and external. These skull images will be especially helpful to you in the laboratory setting. However, they will also be a handy reference for you when you study various structures of the head, such as the eyes and ears, the nasal cavity and paranasal sinuses, the muscles of the head and neck, and the structures of the brain. Our primary focus in this section is on the skull because of its complexity and the difficulty that some students have with skull structure in the absence of a set of good teaching images. We did not include a detailed overview of all the bones of the body here because the best images available are already in your *Anatomy & Physiology, 6th edition* textbook!

Part 3 *Internal Anatomy* provides a survey of helpful images of the inside structures of the body. These images often include representations of dissected organs of many different systems to help you see how they all fit together in the human body. We have also included some casts, images produces by filling up hollow body structures (such as blood vessels) with a substance that hardens to produce a molded casting of what the hollow spaces look like. Such casts help you appreciate body structure in a different way than ordinary anatomical images.

Part 4 *Cross-sectional Anatomy* features an introductory set of horizontal (transverse) sections of the human body. Such sectional views help you develop a stronger sense of the three-dimensional relationships of the various structures of the body. Also included in this section is a set of examples of CT and MRI scans showing cross sections of the body. Because of the increasing importance of cross-sectional anatomy in today's medical imaging, we feel that this resource is an especially useful in helping you apply your understanding human body structure in practical, applied ways.

Part 5 *Histology* is a mini-atlas of some of the major types of tissues found in the body. Our experience as students and teachers tells us that an understanding of tissues, or histology, is a good foundation for easily learning the anatomy of every part of the body. And our experience also tells us that the more examples you see early in your studies, the easier it is to grasp the fundamental concepts of histology. So this section of the Brief Atlas provides a handy set of tissue samples gleaned from the major histology atlases to supplement those already found in *Anatomy & Physiology (6th Edition)*.

We trust that you'll find these carefully selected images helpful in your study of human anatomy and physiology!

Gary A. Thibodeau
Kevin T. Patton

Surface Anatomy

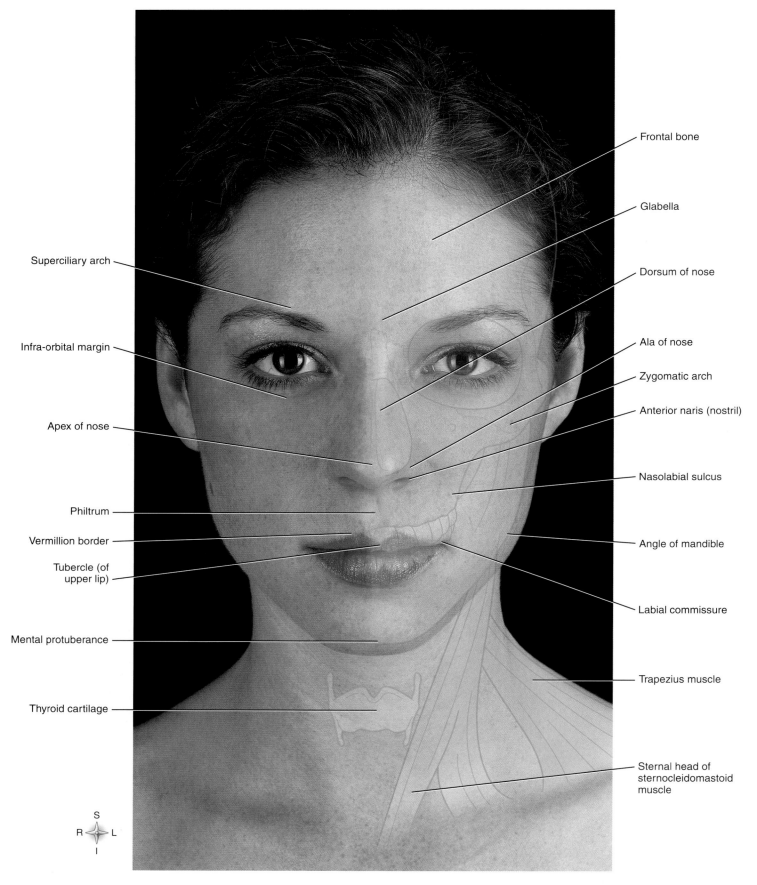

Superciliary arch

Infra-orbital margin

Apex of nose

Philtrum

Vermillion border

Tubercle (of
upper lip)

Mental protuberance

Thyroid cartilage

Frontal bone

Glabella

Dorsum of nose

Ala of nose

Zygomatic arch

Anterior naris (nostril)

Nasolabial sulcus

Angle of mandible

Labial commissure

Trapezius muscle

Sternal head of
sternocleidomastoid
muscle

Figure 1-1 *Surface anatomy of the face (anterior view).*

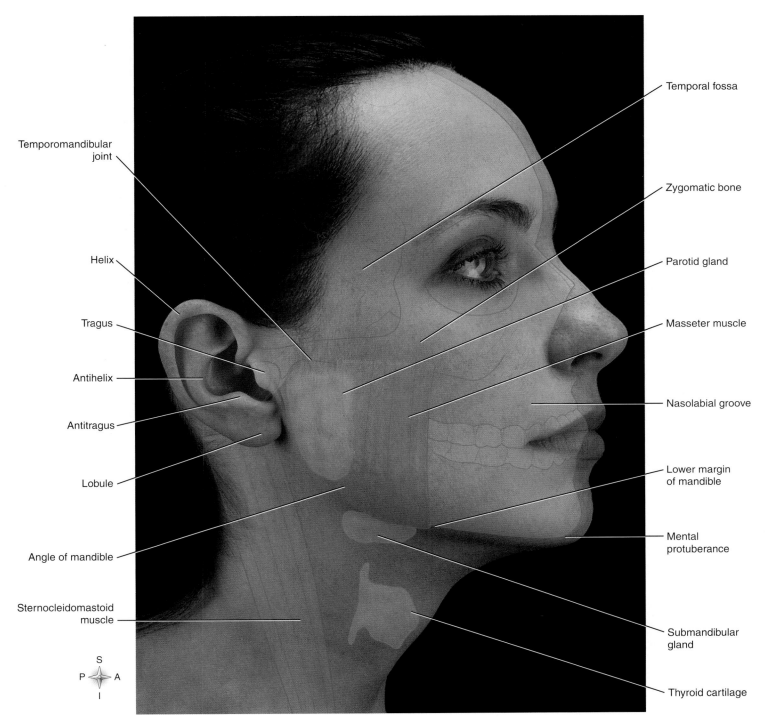

Temporal fossa

Zygomatic bone

Parotid gland

Masseter muscle

Nasolabial groove

Lower margin
of mandible

Mental
protuberance

Submandibular
gland

Thyroid cartilage

Temporomandibular
joint

Helix

Tragus

Antihelix

Antitragus

Lobule

Angle of mandible

Sternocleidomastoid
muscle

S
P A
I

Figure 1-2 *Surface anatomy of the face (lateral view).*

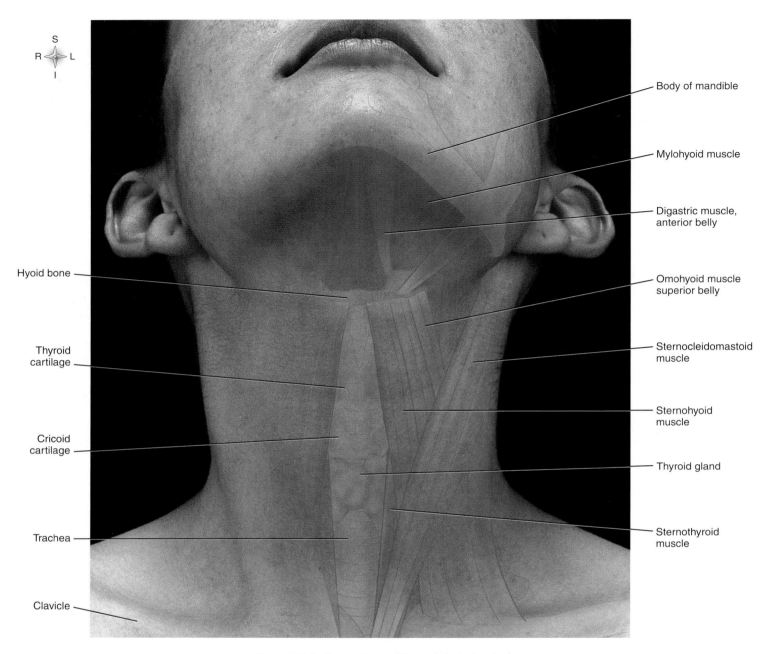

Figure 1-3 *Surface anatomy of the neck (anterior view)*

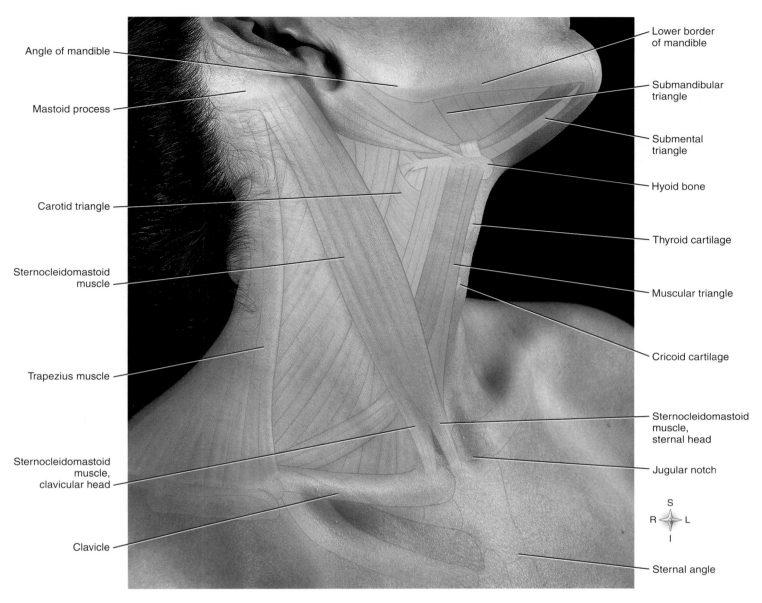

Angle of mandible

Mastoid process

Carotid triangle

Sternocleidomastoid muscle

Trapezius muscle

Sternocleidomastoid muscle, clavicular head

Clavicle

Lower border of mandible

Submandibular triangle

Submental triangle

Hyoid bone

Thyroid cartilage

Muscular triangle

Cricoid cartilage

Sternocleidomastoid muscle, sternal head

Jugular notch

Sternal angle

Figure 1-4 *Surface anatomy of the neck (oblique view)*

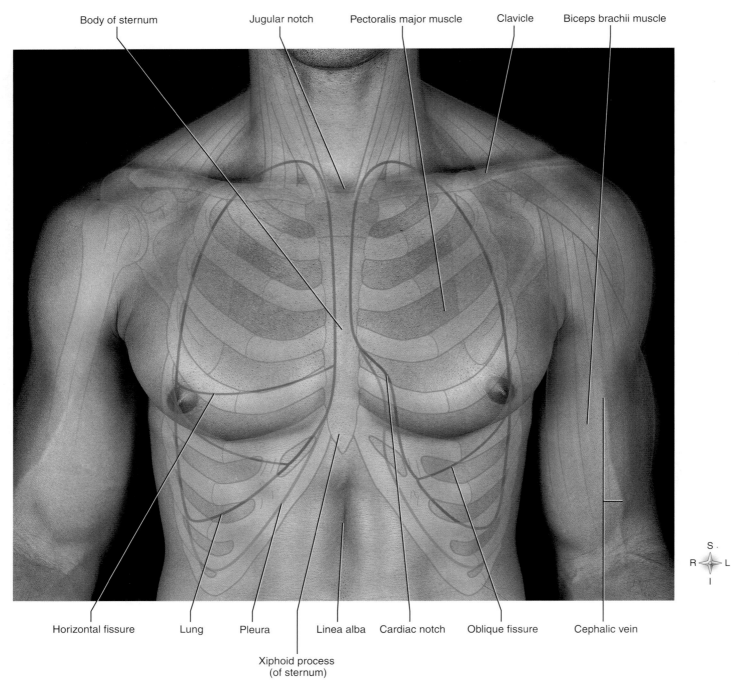

Body of sternum

Jugular notch

Pectoralis major muscle

Clavicle

Biceps brachii muscle

Horizontal fissure

Lung

Pleura

Linea alba

Cardiac notch

Oblique fissure

Cephalic vein

Xiphoid process
(of sternum)

Figure 1-5 *Surface anatomy of the thorax (anterior view)*

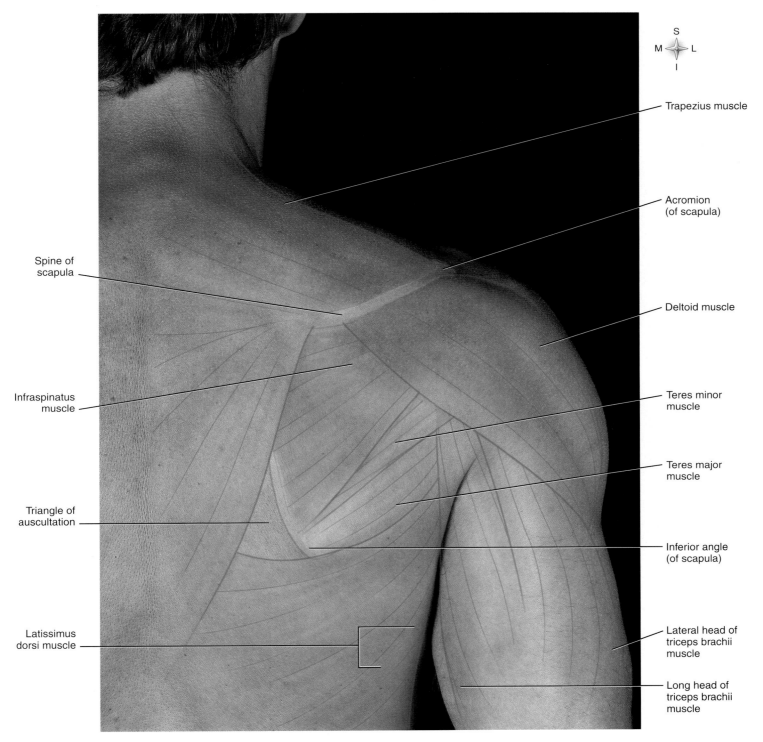

Trapezius muscle

Acromion
(of scapula)

Spine of
scapula

Deltoid muscle

Infraspinatus
muscle

Teres minor
muscle

Teres major
muscle

Triangle of
auscultation

Inferior angle
(of scapula)

Latissimus
dorsi muscle

Lateral head of
triceps brachii
muscle

Long head of
triceps brachii
muscle

Figure 1-6 *Surface anatomy of the shoulder (posterior view)*

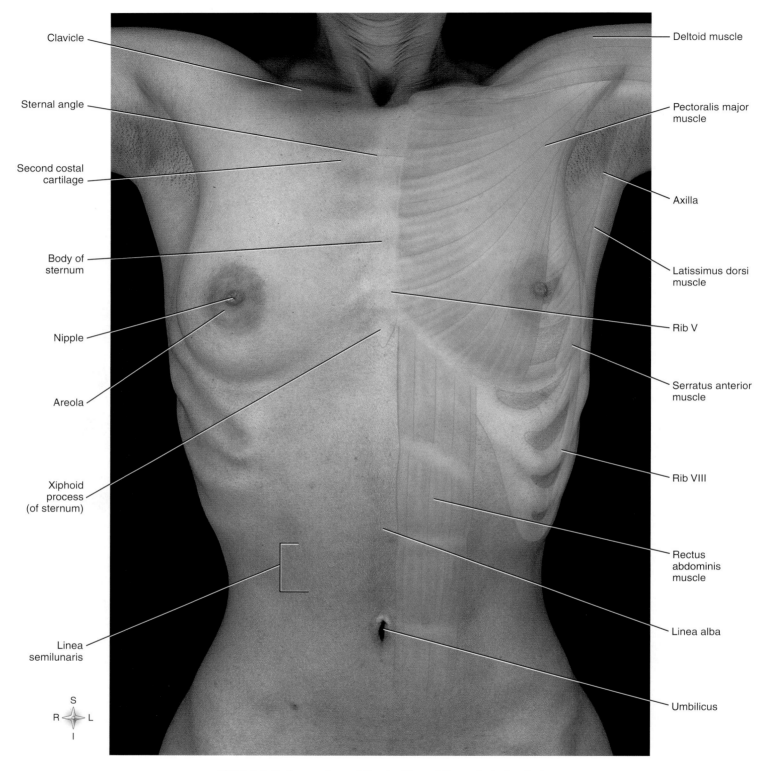

Clavicle

Sternal angle

Second costal
cartilage

Body of
sternum

Nipple

Areola

Xiphoid
process
(of sternum)

Linea
semilunaris

Deltoid muscle

Pectoralis major
muscle

Axilla

Latissimus dorsi
muscle

Rib V

Serratus anterior
muscle

Rib VIII

Rectus
abdominis
muscle

Linea alba

Umbilicus

S
R ◆ L
I

Figure 1-7 *Surface anatomy of the shoulder and thorax (anterior view).*

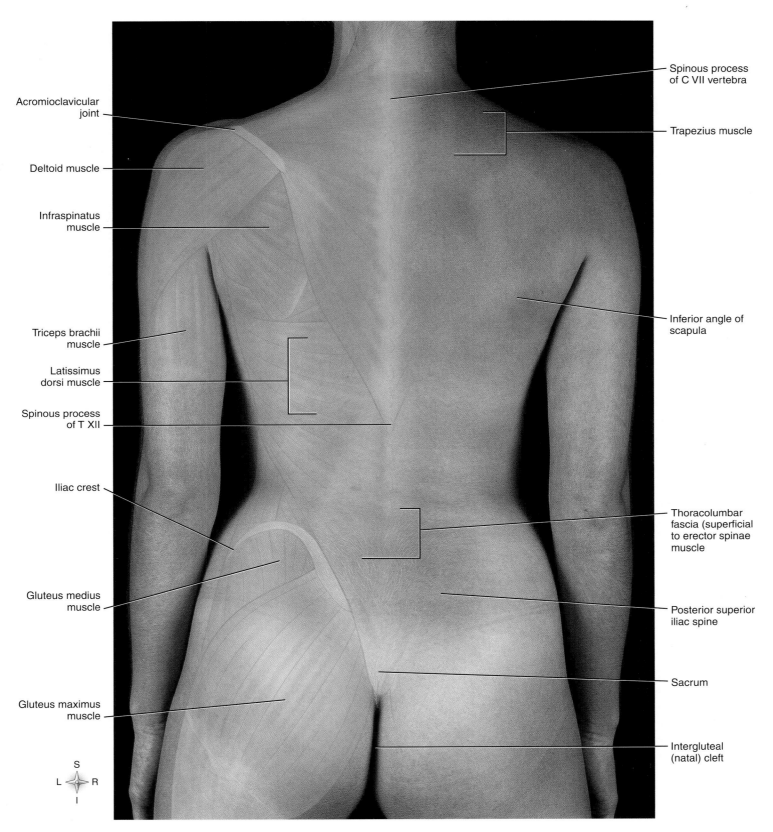

Acromioclavicular joint

Deltoid muscle

Infraspinatus muscle

Triceps brachii muscle

Latissimus dorsi muscle

Spinous process of T XII

Iliac crest

Gluteus medius muscle

Gluteus maximus muscle

Spinous process of C VII vertebra

Trapezius muscle

Inferior angle of scapula

Thoracolumbar fascia (superficial to erector spinae muscle

Posterior superior iliac spine

Sacrum

Intergluteal (natal) cleft

S
L —✦— R
I

Figure 1-8 *Surface anatomy of the shoulders, thorax, and hips (posterior view).*

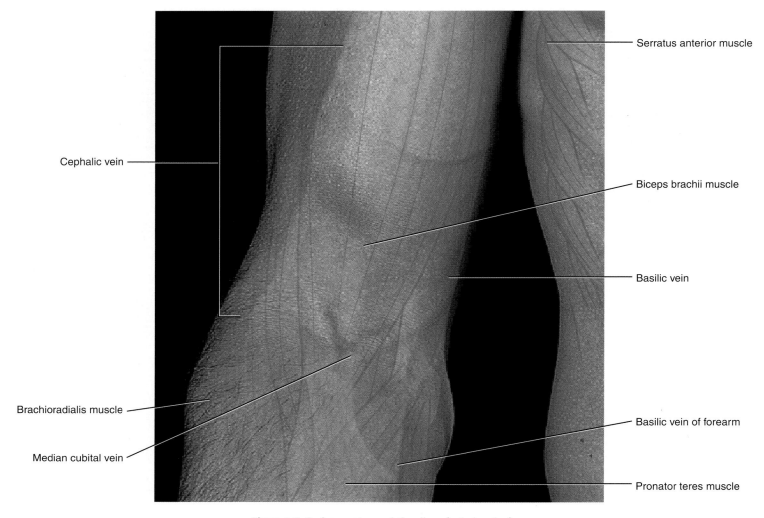

Serratus anterior muscle

Cephalic vein

Biceps brachii muscle

Basilic vein

Brachioradialis muscle

Basilic vein of forearm

Median cubital vein

Pronator teres muscle

Figure 1-9 *Surface anatomy of the elbow (anterior view).*

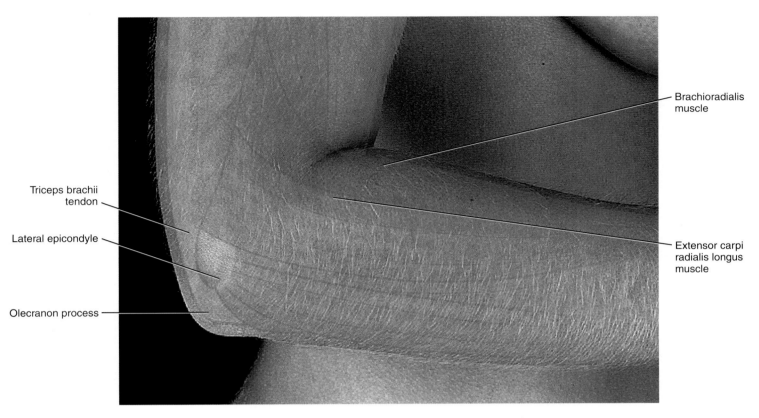

Brachioradialis muscle

Triceps brachii tendon

Lateral epicondyle

Olecranon process

Extensor carpi radialis longus muscle

Figure 1-10 *Surface anatomy of the elbow (flexed; lateral view).*

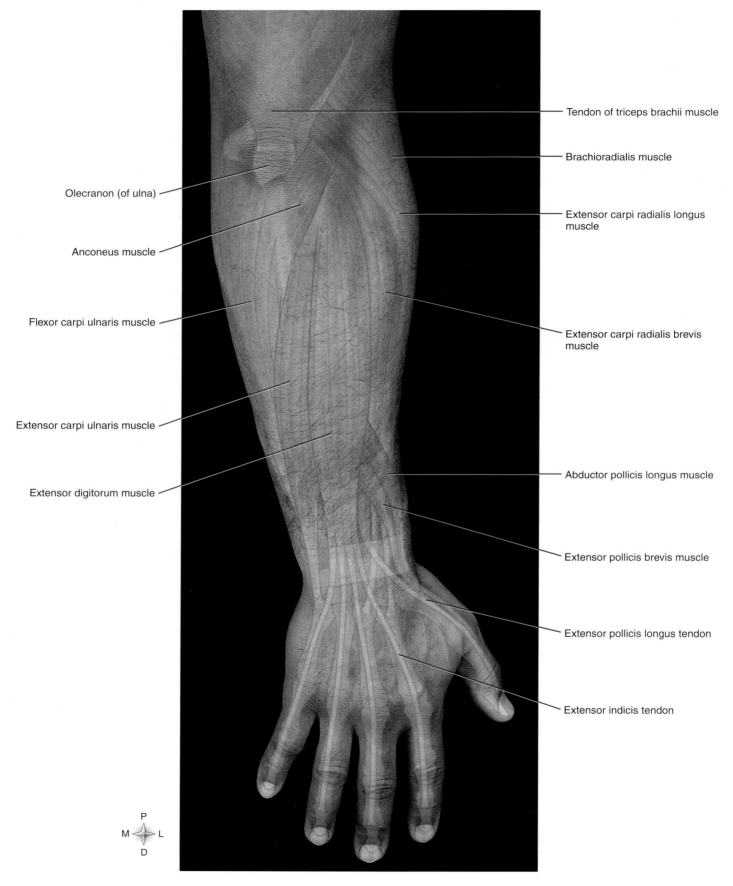

Tendon of triceps brachii muscle

Brachioradialis muscle

Extensor carpi radialis longus
muscle

Olecranon (of ulna)

Anconeus muscle

Extensor carpi radialis brevis
muscle

Flexor carpi ulnaris muscle

Extensor carpi ulnaris muscle

Extensor digitorum muscle

Abductor pollicis longus muscle

Extensor pollicis brevis muscle

Extensor pollicis longus tendon

Extensor indicis tendon

P
M ✦ L
D

Figure 1-11 *Surface anatomy of the elbow and forearm (dorsal view).*

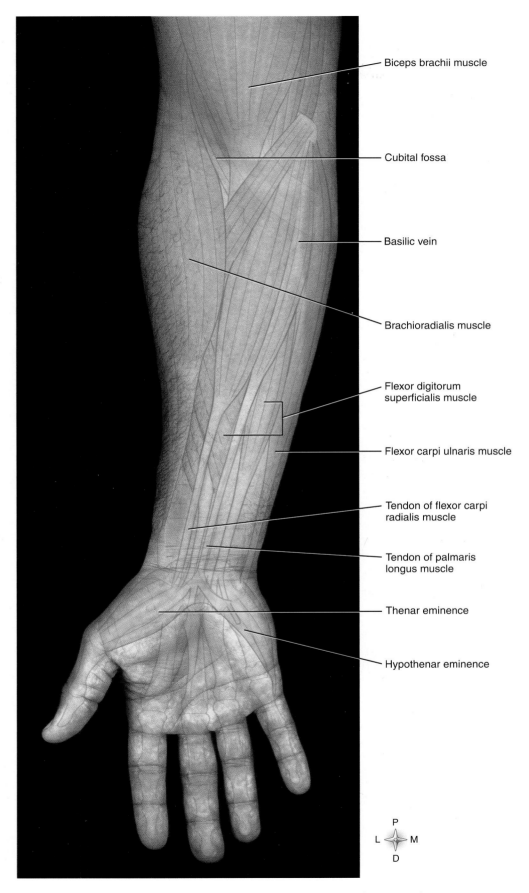

Biceps brachii muscle

Cubital fossa

Basilic vein

Brachioradialis muscle

Flexor digitorum superficialis muscle

Flexor carpi ulnaris muscle

Tendon of flexor carpi radialis muscle

Tendon of palmaris longus muscle

Thenar eminence

Hypothenar eminence

P
L — M
D

Figure 1-12 *Surface anatomy of the elbow and forearm (ventral view).*

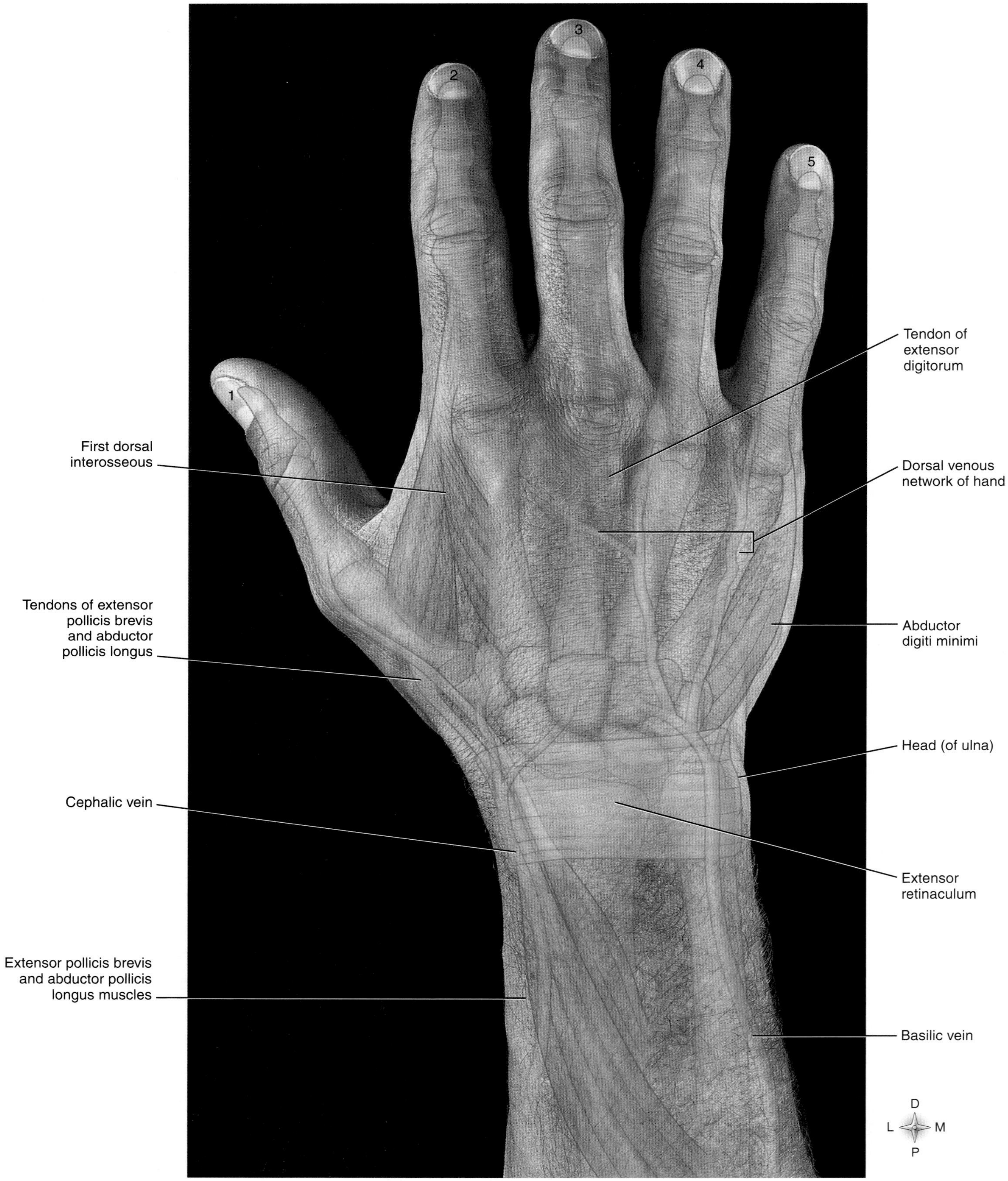
1
2
3
4
5
Tendon of extensor digitorum
First dorsal interosseous
Dorsal venous network of hand
Tendons of extensor pollicis brevis and abductor pollicis longus
Abductor digiti minimi
Head (of ulna)
Cephalic vein
Extensor retinaculum
Extensor pollicis brevis and abductor pollicis longus muscles
Basilic vein
D
L
M
P

Figure 1-13 ***Surface anatomy of the hand and wrist (dorsal view).***

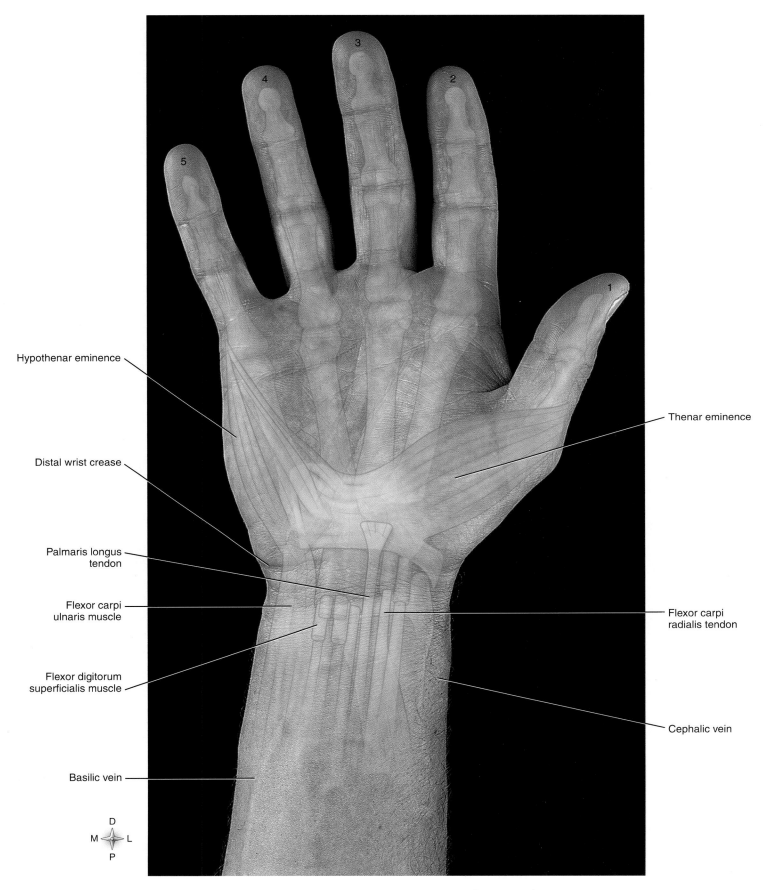

Hypothenar eminence

Distal wrist crease

Palmaris longus
tendon

Flexor carpi
ulnaris muscle

Flexor digitorum
superficialis muscle

Basilic vein

Thenar eminence

Flexor carpi
radialis tendon

Cephalic vein

D
M ✦ L
P

Figure 1-14 *Surface anatomy of the hand and wrist (ventral view).*

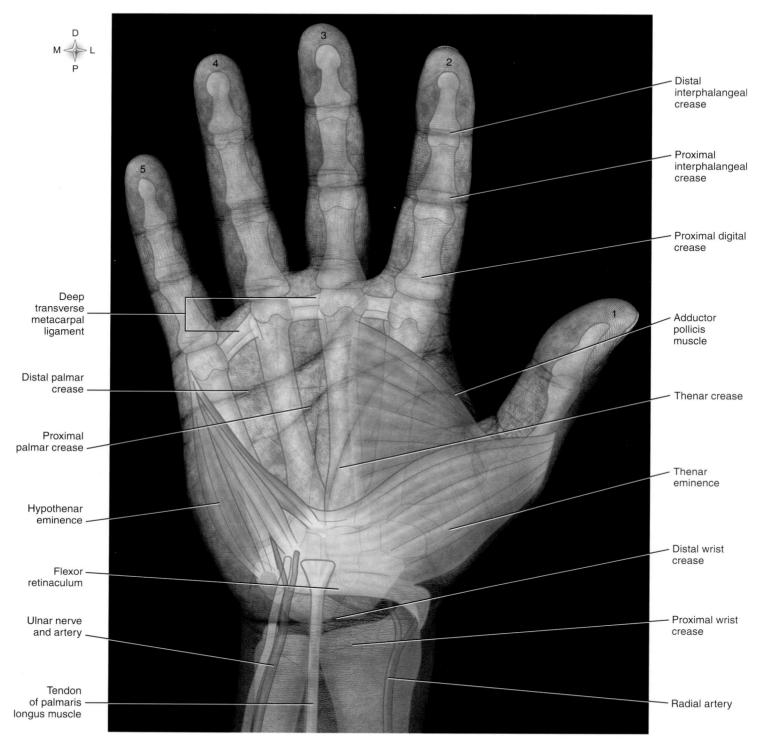

Figure 1-15 *Surface anatomy of the hand and wrist (deep; ventral view).*

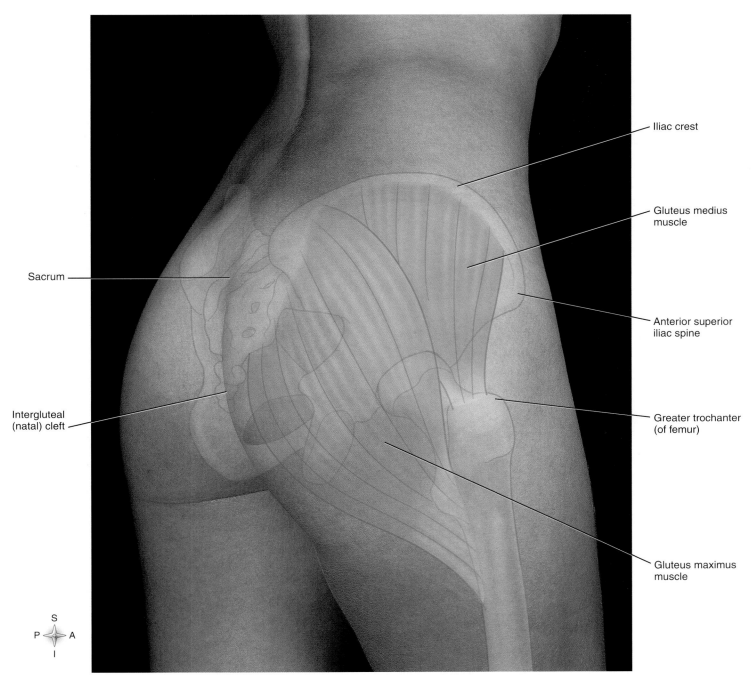

Iliac crest

Gluteus medius
muscle

Anterior superior
iliac spine

Greater trochanter
(of femur)

Gluteus maximus
muscle

Sacrum

Intergluteal
(natal) cleft

S
P A
I

Figure 1-16 *Surface anatomy of the hip (lateral view).*

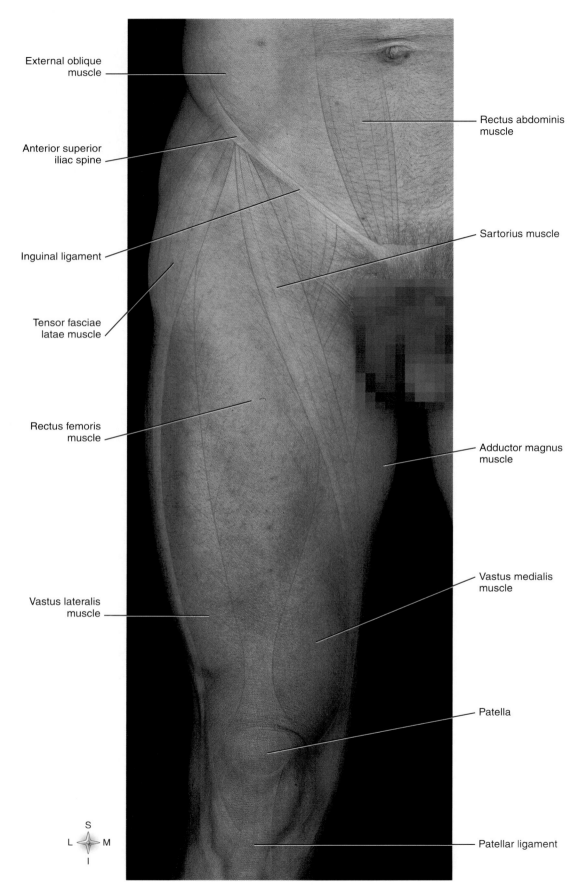

External oblique muscle

Anterior superior iliac spine

Inguinal ligament

Tensor fasciae latae muscle

Rectus femoris muscle

Vastus lateralis muscle

Rectus abdominis muscle

Sartorius muscle

Adductor magnus muscle

Vastus medialis muscle

Patella

Patellar ligament

S
L — M
I

Figure 1-17 *Surface anatomy of the hip and thigh (anterior view).*

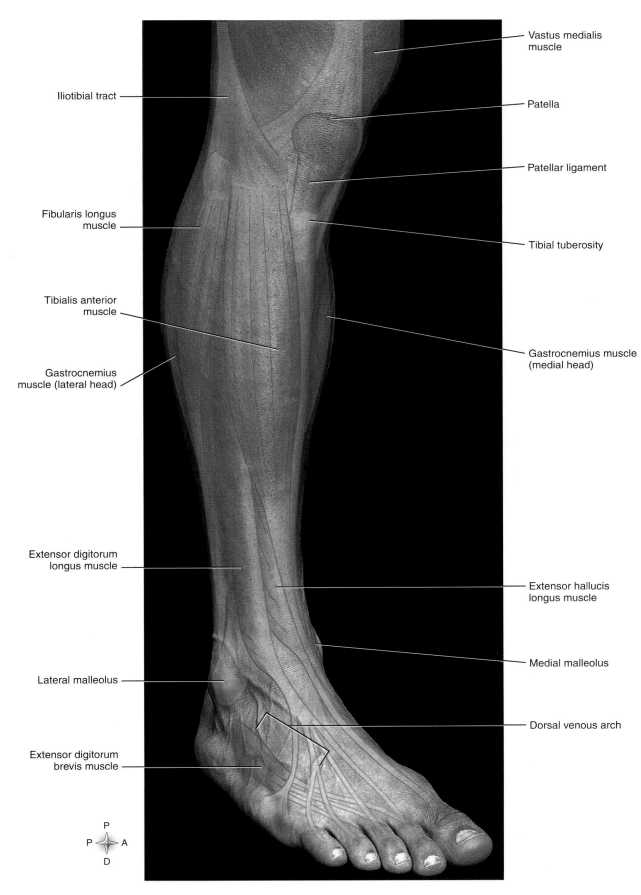

Iliotibial tract

Fibularis longus
muscle

Tibialis anterior
muscle

Gastrocnemius
muscle (lateral head)

Extensor digitorum
longus muscle

Lateral malleolus

Extensor digitorum
brevis muscle

Vastus medialis
muscle

Patella

Patellar ligament

Tibial tuberosity

Gastrocnemius muscle
(medial head)

Extensor hallucis
longus muscle

Medial malleolus

Dorsal venous arch

Figure 1-18 *Surface anatomy of the knee and leg (oblique view).*

Calcaneal tendon   Fibularis brevis tendon   Extensor hallucis longus tendon

Fibularis longus tendon   Extensor digitorum longus tendon   Tibialis anterior tendon

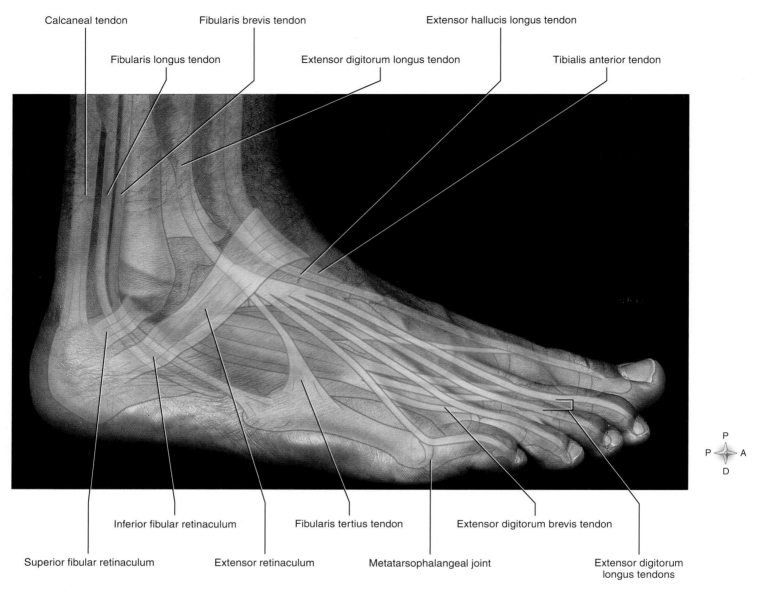

Inferior fibular retinaculum   Fibularis tertius tendon   Extensor digitorum brevis tendon

Superior fibular retinaculum   Extensor retinaculum   Metatarsophalangeal joint   Extensor digitorum longus tendons

Figure 1-19 *Surface anatomy of the ankle and foot (lateral view).*

Extensor hallucis longus tendon

Extensor retinaculum

Fibular retinaculum

Calcaneal tendon

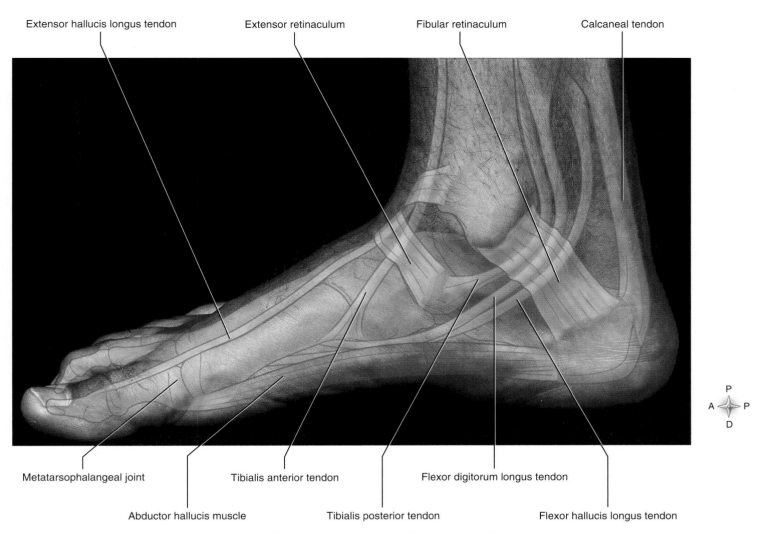

Metatarsophalangeal joint

Abductor hallucis muscle

Tibialis anterior tendon

Tibialis posterior tendon

Flexor digitorum longus tendon

Flexor hallucis longus tendon

Figure 1-20 *Surface anatomy of the ankle and foot (medial view).*

PART 2

Skeleton

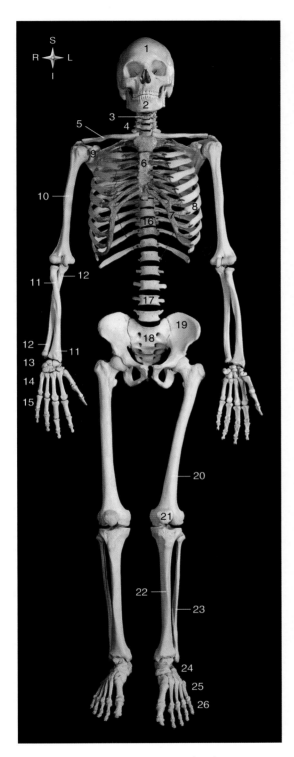

Figure 2-1 *Skeleton, Anterior view.*

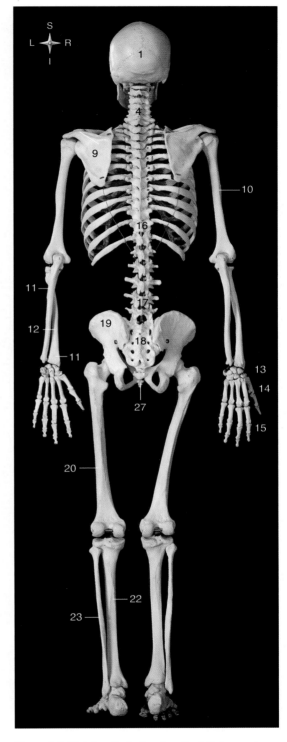

Figure 2-2 *Skeleton, Posterior view.* The left forearm is supinated and the right forearm is pronated.

1 Skull
2 Mandible
3 Hyoid bone
4 Cervical vertebrae
5 Clavicle
6 Sternum
7 Costal Cartilages

8 Ribs
9 Scapula
10 Humerus
11 Radius
12 Ulna
13 Carpal bones
14 Metacarpal bones

15 Phalanges of thumb
   and fingers
16 Thoracic vertebrae
17 Lumbar vertebrae
18 Sacrum
19 Hip bone
20 Femur

21 Patella
22 Tibia
23 Fibula
24 Tarsal bones
25 Metatarsal bones
26 Phalanges of toes
27 Coccyx

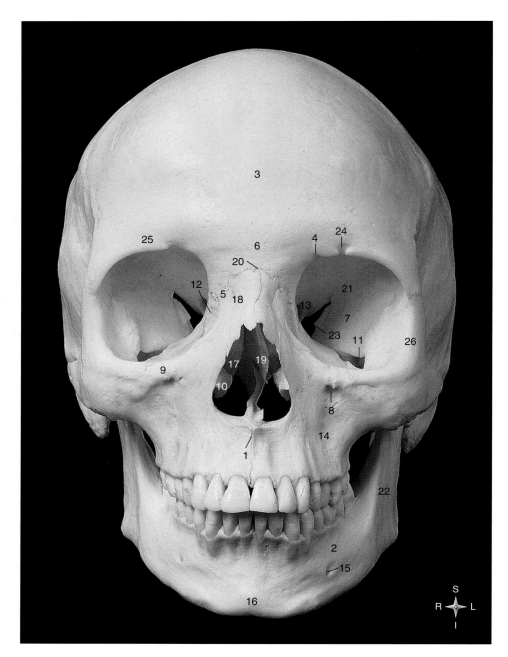

1 Anterior nasal spine
2 Body of mandible
3 Frontal bone
4 Frontal notch
5 Frontal process of maxilla
6 Glabella
7 Greater wing of sphenoid
  bone
8 Infraorbital foramen
9 Infraorbital margin

10 Inferior nasal concha
11 Inferior orbital fissure
12 Lacrimal bone
13 Lesser wing of sphenoid
  bone
14 Maxilla
15 Mental foramen
16 Mental protuberance
17 Middle nasal concha
18 Nasal bone

19 Nasal septum
20 Nasion
21 Orbit (orbital cavity)
22 Ramus of mandible
23 Superior orbital fissure
24 Supraorbital foramen
25 Supraorbital margin
26 Zygomatic bone

Figure 2-3 *Skull (frontal view)*

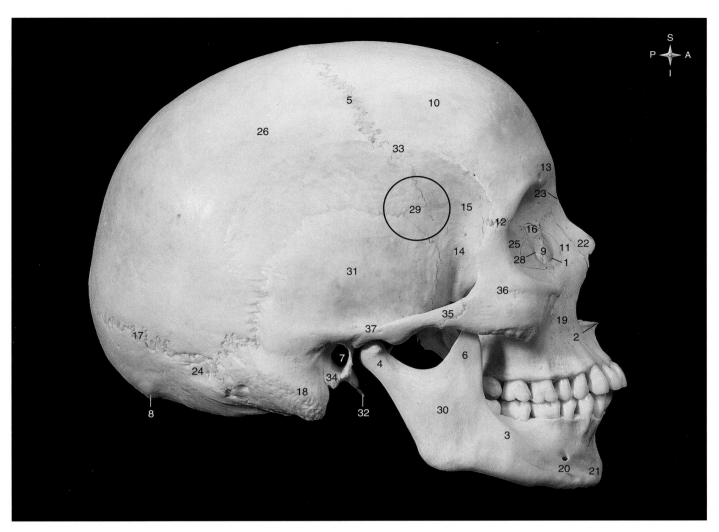

Figure 2-4 *Skull (right, lateral view).*

1 Anterior lacrimal crest
2 Anterior nasal spine
3 Body of mandible
4 Condyle of mandible
5 Coronal suture
6 Coronoid process of mandible
7 External acoustic meatus of temporal bone
8 External occipital protuberance (inion)
9 Fossa for lacrimal sac
10 Frontal bone

11 Frontal process of maxilla
12 Frontozygomatic suture
13 Glabella
14 Greater wing of sphenoid bone
15 Inferior temporal line
16 Lacrimal bone
17 Lambdoid suture
18 Mastoid process of temporal bone
19 Maxilla
20 Mental foramen

21 Mental protuberance
22 Nasal bone
23 Nasion
24 Occipital bone
25 Orbital part of ethmoid bone
26 Parietal bone
27 Pituitary fossa (sella turcica)
28 Posterior lacrimal crest
29 Pterion (encircled)
30 Ramus of mandible
31 Squamous part of temporal bone

32 Styloid process of temporal bone
33 Superior temporal line
34 Tympanic part of temporal bone
35 Zygomatic arch
36 Zygomatic bone
37 Zygomatic process of temporal bone

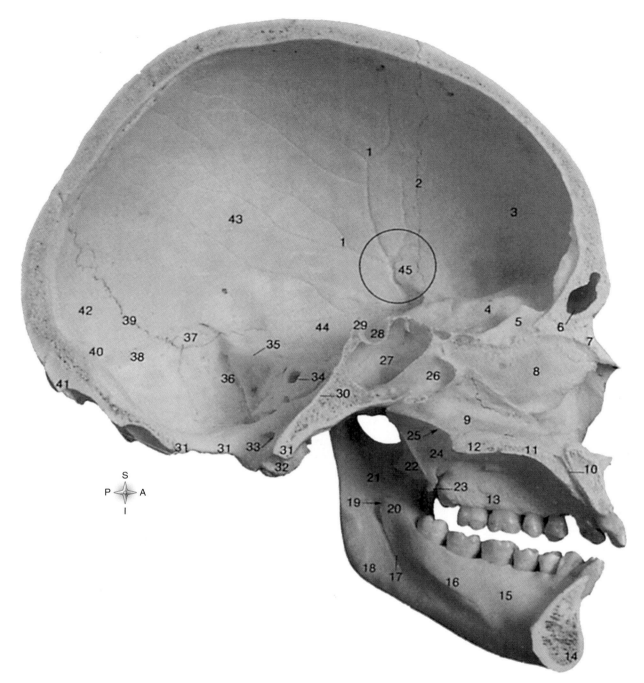

Figure 2-5 *Left half of the skull. Sagittal section.*

1 Grooves for middle meningeal vessels
2 Coronal suture
3 Squamous part of frontal bone
4 Orbital part of frontal bone
5 Cristal galli of ethmoid bone
6 Frontal sinus
7 Nasal bone
8 Perpendicular plate of ethmoid bone
9 Vomer
10 Incisive canal
11 Palatine process of maxilla
12 Palatine process of maxilla

13 Alveolar process of maxilla
14 Mental protuberance
15 Body of mandible
16 Mylohyoid line
17 Groove for mylohyoid nerve
18 Angle of mandible
19 Mandibular foramen
20 Lingula
21 Ramus of mandible
22 Lateral pterygoid plate
23 Pterygoid hamulus of medial pterygoid plate
24 Medial pterygoid plate
25 Posterior nasal aperture

26 Right sphenoidal sinus
27 Left sphenoidal sinus
28 Pituitary fossa (sella turcica)
29 Dorsum sellae
30 Clivus
31 Margin of foraman magnum
32 Occipital condyle
33 Hypoglossal canal
34 Internal acoustic meatus in petrous part of temporal bone
35 Groove for superior petrosal sinus

36 Groove for sigmoid sinus
37 Mastoid (posterior inferior) angle of parietal bone
38 Groove for transverse sinus
39 Lambdoidal suture
40 Internal occipital protuberance
41 External occipital protuberance
42 Occipital bone
43 Parietal bone
44 Squamous part of temporal bone
45 Pterion (encircled)

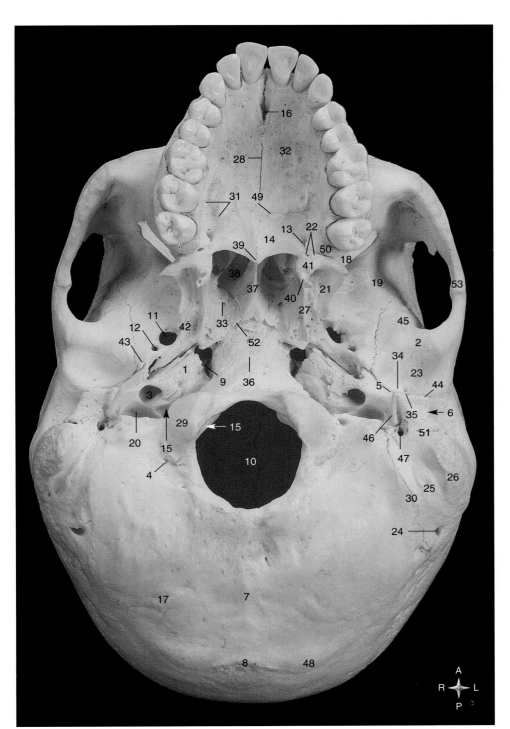

1 Apex of petrous part of temporal bone
2 Articular tubercle
3 Carotid canal
4 Condylar canal (posterior)
5 Edge of tegmen tympani
6 External acoustic meatus
7 External occipital crest
8 External occipital protuberance
9 Foramen lacerum
10 Foramen magnum
11 Foramen ovale
12 Foramen spinosum
13 Greater palatine foramen
14 Horizontal plate of palatine bone
15 Hypoglossal (anterior condylar) canal
16 Incisive fossa
17 Inferior nuchal line
18 Inferior orbital fissure
19 Infratemporal crest of greater wing of sphenoid bone
20 Jugular foramen
21 Lateral pterygoid plate
22 Lesser palatine foramina
23 Mandibular fossa
24 Mastoid foramen
25 Mastoid notch
26 Mastoid process
27 Medial pterygoid plate
28 Median palatine (intermaxillary) suture
29 Occipital condyle
30 Occipital groove
31 Palatine grooves and spines
32 Palatine process of maxilla
33 Palatinovaginal canal
34 Petrosquamous fissure
35 Petrotympanic fissue
36 Pharyngeal tubercle
37 Posterior border of vomer
38 Posterior nasal aperture (choana)
39 Posterior nasal spine
40 Pterygoid hamulus
41 Pyramidal process of palatine bone
42 Scaphoid fossa
43 Spine of sphenoid bone
44 Squamotympanic fissure
45 Squamous part of temporal bone
46 Styloid process
47 Stylomastoid foramen
48 Superior nuchal line
49 Transverse palatine (palatomaxillary) suture
50 Tuberosity of maxilla
51 Tympanic part of temporal bone
52 Vomerovaginal canal
53 Zygomatic arch

Figure 2-6 *Skull (external surface of the base)*

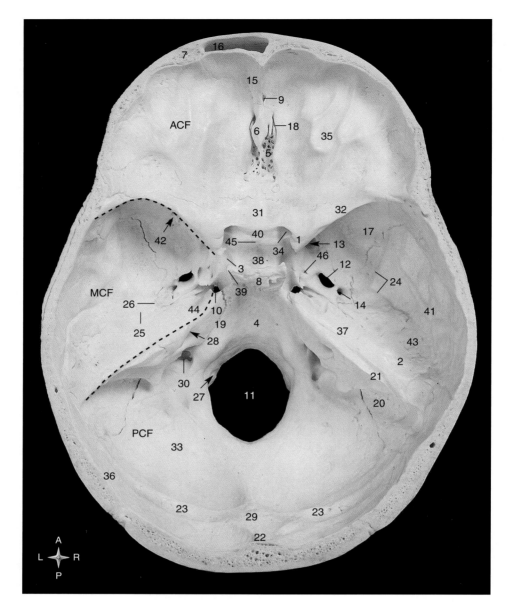

1 Anterior clinoid process
2 Arcuate eminence
3 Carotid groove
4 Clivus
5 Cribriform plate of ethmoid bone
6 Crista galli
7 Diploë
8 Dorsum sellae
9 Foramen cecum
10 Foramen lacerum
11 Foramen magnum
12 Foramen ovale
13 Foramen rotundum
14 Foramen spinosum
15 Frontal crest
16 Frontal sinus
17 Greater wing of sphenoid bone
18 Groove for anterior ethmoidal nerve and vessels
19 Groove for inferior petrosal sinus

20 Groove for sigmoid sinus
21 Groove for superior petrosal sinus
22 Groove for superior sagittal sinus
23 Groove for transverse sinus
24 Grooves for middle meningeal vessels
25 Hiatus and groove for greater petrosal nerve
26 Hiatus and groove for lesser petrosal nerve
27 Hypoglossal canal
28 Internal acoustic meatus
29 Internal occipital protuberance
30 Jugular foramen
31 Jugum of sphenoid bone
32 Lesser wing of sphenoid bone
33 Occipital bone
34 Optic canal

35 Orbital part of frontal bone
36 Parietal bone (postero-inferior angle only)
37 Petrous part of temporal bone
38 Pituitary fossa (sella turcica)
39 Posterior clinoid process
40 Prechiasmatic groove
41 Squamous part of temporal bone
42 Superior orbital fissure
43 Tegmen tympani
44 Trigeminal impression
45 Tuberculum sellae
46 Venous foramen

ACF, Anterior cranial fossa
MCF, Middle cranial fossa
PCF, Posterior cranial fossa

Figure 2-7 *Skull (internal surface of the base)*

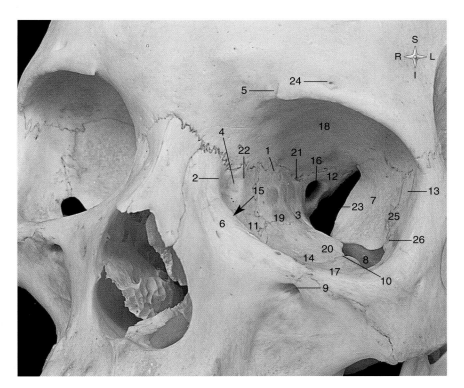

1 Anterior ethmoidal foramen
2 Anterior lacrimal crest
3 Body of sphenoid bone, forming medial wall
4 Fossa for lacrimal sac
5 Frontal notch
6 Frontal process of maxilla, forming medial wall
7 Greater wing of sphenoid bone, forming lateral wall
8 Inferior orbital fissure
9 Infraorbital foramen
10 Infraorbital groove
11 Lacrimal bone, forming medial wall
12 Lesser wing of sphenoid bone, forming roof
13 Marginal tubercle
14 Maxilla, forming floor
15 Nasolacrimal canal
16 Optic canal
17 Orbital border of zygomatic bone, forming floor
18 Orbital part of frontal bone, forming roof
19 Orbital plate of ethmoid bone, forming medial wall
20 Orbital process of palatine bone, forming floor
21 Posterior ethmoidal foramen
22 Posterior lacrimal crest
23 Superior orbital fissure
24 Supraorbital foramen
25 Zygomatic bone forming lateral wall
26 Zygomatico-orbital foramen

Figure 2-8 *Skull (bones of the eye orbit)*

1 Air cells of ethmoidal sinus
2 Clivus
3 Cribriform plate of ethmoid bone
4 Dorsum sellae
5 Ethmoidal bulla
6 Frontal sinus
7 Horizontal plate of palatine bone
8 Incisive canal
9 Inferior meatus
10 Inferior nasal concha
11 Lateral pterygoid plate
12 Left sphenoidal sinus
13 Medial pterygoid plate
14 Nasal bone
15 Nasal spine of frontal bone
16 Opening of maxillary sinus
17 Palatine process of maxilla
18 Perpendicular plate of palatine bone
19 Pituitary fossa (sella turcica)
20 Pterygoid hamulus
21 Right sphenoidal sinus
22 Semilunar hiatus
23 Sphenopalatine foramen
24 Uncinate process of ethmoid bone

Figure 2-9 *Nasal cavity (lateral wall)*

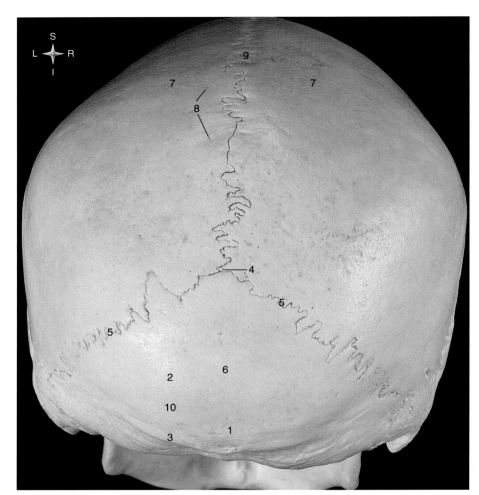

1 External occipital protuberance (inion)
2 Highest nuchal line
3 Inferior nuchal line
4 Lambda
5 Lambdoid suture
6 Occipital bone
7 Parietal bone
8 Parietal foramen
9 Sagittal suture
10 Superior nuchal line

Figure 2-10 *Skull (posterior view).*

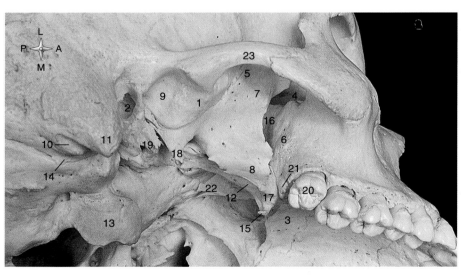

1 Articular tubercle
2 External acoustic meatus
3 Horizontal plate of palatine bone
4 Inferior orbital fissure
5 Infratemporal crest
6 Infratemporal (posterior) surface of maxilla
7 Infratemporal surface of greater wing of sphenoid bone
8 Lateral pterygoid plate
9 Mandibular fossa
10 Mastoid notch
11 Mastoid process
12 Medial pterygoid plate
13 Occipital condyle
14 Occipital groove
15 Pterygoid hamulus
16 Pterygomaxillary fissure and pterygopalatine fossa
17 Pyramidal process of palatine bone
18 Spine of sphenoid bone
19 Styloid process and sheath
20 Third molar tooth
21 Tubersoity of maxilla
22 Vomer
23 Zygomatic arch

Figure 2-11 *Skull (oblique inferior view)*

Internal Anatomy

1 Left frontal sinus
2 Left ethmoidal air cells
3 Falx cerebri
4 Medial surface of right cerebral hemisphere
5 Anterior cerebral artery
6 Corpus callosum
7 Arachnoid granulations
8 Superior sagittal sinus
9 Tentorium cerebelli
10 Straight sinus
11 Cerebellum
12 Great cerebral vein
13 Midbrain
14 Pons
15 Fourth ventricle
16 Medulla oblongata
17 Margin of foramen
   magnum
18 Cerebellomedullary
   cistern (cisterna
   magna)
19 Posterior arch of
   atlas
20 Spinal cord
21 Intervertebral disc
   between axis and
   third cervical vertebra
22 Laryngopharynx
23 Inlet of larynx
24 Thyroid cartilage
25 Hyoid bone
26 Epiglottis
27 Vallecula
28 Oropharynx
29 Tongue
30 Mandible
31 Hard palate
32 Soft palate
33 Nasopharynx
34 Dens of axis
35 Anterior arch of atlas
36 Pharyngeal tonsil
37 Opening of auditory tube
38 Choana (posterior nasal
   aperture)
39 Nasal septum
40 Sphenoidal sinus
41 Pituitary gland
42 Optic chiasma

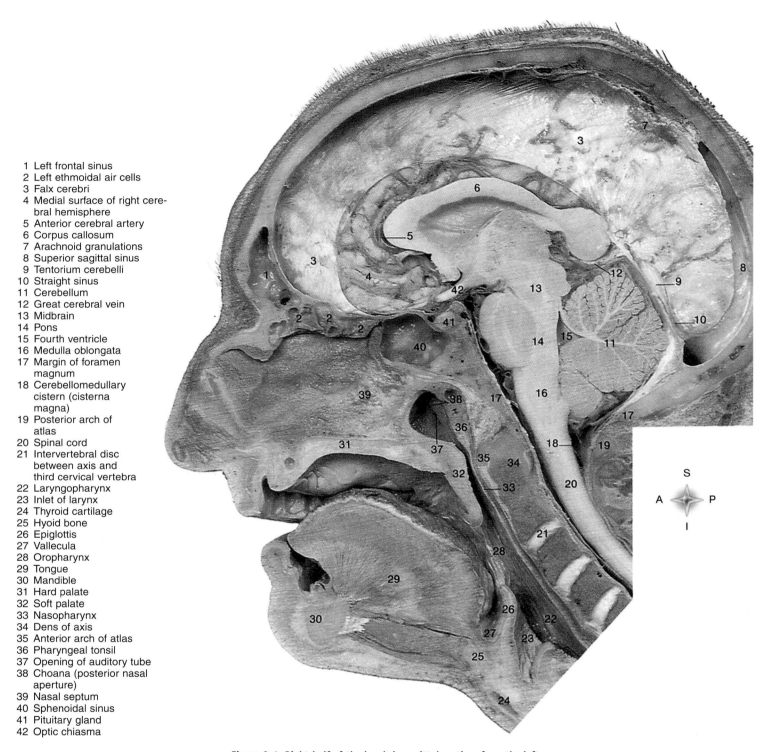

Figure 3-1 *Right half of the head, in sagittal section, from the left*

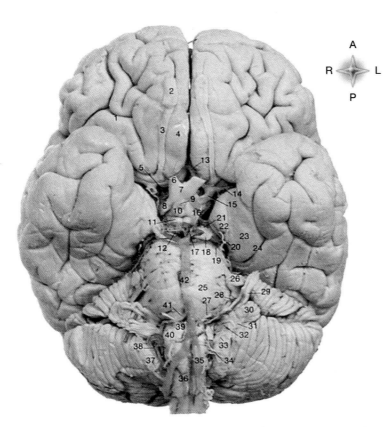

1 Orbital sulcus
2 Olfactory bulb
3 Olfactory tract
4 Gyrus rectus
5 Anterior perforated substance
6 Optic nerve
7 Optic chiasma
8 Optic tract
9 Pituitary stalk (infundibulum)
10 Tuber cinereum and median eminence
11 Mamillary body
12 Posterior perforated substance
13 Anterior cerebral artery
14 Middle cerebral artery
15 Internal carotid artery
16 Posterior communicating artery
17 Posterior cerebral artery
18 Oculomotor nerve
19 Superior cerebellar artery
20 Trochlear nerve
21 Crus of cerebral peduncle
22 Uncus
23 Parahippocampal gyrus

24 Collateral sulcus
25 Pons
26 Trigeminal nerve
27 Abducens nerve
28 Facial nerve
29 Vestibulocochlear nerve
30 Flocculus of cerebellum
31 Choroid plexus from lateral recess of fourth ventricle
32 Roots of glossopharyngeal, vagus and accessory nerves
33 Spinal part of accessory nerve
34 Rootlets of hypoglossal nerve (superficial to marker)
35 Vertebral artery
36 Medulla oblongata
37 Tonsil of cerebellum
38 Posterior inferior cerebellar artery
39 Pyramid } of medulla
40 Olive } oblongata
41 Anterior inferior cerebellar artery
42 Basilar artery

Figure 3-2 *Brain, from below.*

1 Anterior cerebral artery
2 Rostrum ⎫
3 Genu ⎬ of corpus callosum
4 Body ⎭
5 Cingulate gyrus
6 Precentral gyrus
7 Central sulcus
8 Postcentral gyrus
9 Parietooccipital sulcus
10 Calcarine sulcus
11 Lingual gyrus
12 Cerebellum
13 Medulla oblongata
14 Median aperture of fourth ventricle
15 Fourth ventricle
16 Pons
17 Basilar artery
18 Tegmentum ⎫
19 Aqueduct ⎬ of midbrain
20 Inferior colliculus ⎪
21 Superior colliculus ⎭
22 Posterior commissure
23 Pineal body
24 Suprapineal recess
25 Great cerebral vein
26 Splenium of corpus callosum

27 Fornix
28 Cut edge of septum pellucidum
29 Body of lateral ventricle
30 Thalamus
31 Interthalamic connection
32 Hypothalamic sulcus
33 Hypothalamus
34 Posterior perforated substance
35 Mamillary body
36 Tuber cinereum and median eminence
37 Infundibular recess (base of pituitary stalk)
38 Optic chiasma
39 Supraoptic recess
40 Lamina terminalis
41 Anterior commissure
42 Anterior column of fornix
43 Interventricular foramen and choroid plexus

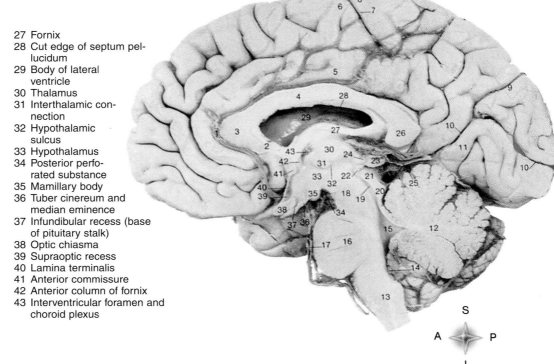

Figure 3-3 *Right half of the brain, in a midline sagittal section, from the left*

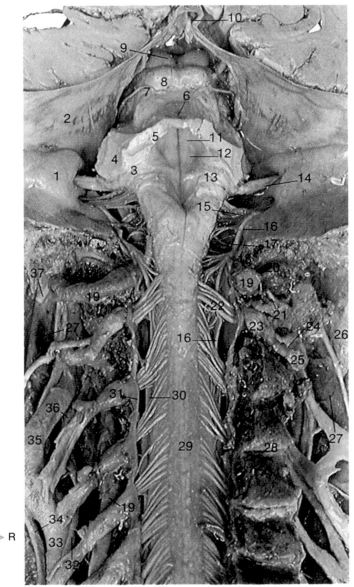

1 Petrous part of temporal bone
2 Tentorium cerebelli
3 Inferior ⎫
4 Middle ⎬ cerebellar peduncle
5 Superior ⎭
6 Superior medullary velum
7 Trochlear nerve
8 Inferior ⎫ colliculus
9 Superior ⎭
10 Straight sinus
11 Medial eminence
12 Facial colliculus
13 Medullary striae
14 Facial and vestibulocochlear nerves and internal acoustic meatus
15 Glossopharyngeal, vagus, and accessory nerves and jugular foramen
16 Spinal part of accessory nerve
17 Rootlets of hypoglossal nerve and hypoglossal canal
18 Margin of foramen magnum
19 Vertebral artery
20 Lateral mass of atlas
21 Ventral ramus of first cervical nerve
22 Dorsal rootlets ⎫
23 Dorsal root ganglion ⎬ of second cervical nerve
24 Ventral ramus ⎪
25 Dorsal ramus ⎭
26 Posterior belly of digastric muscle
27 Internal jugular vein
28 Zygapophyseal joint
29 Spinal cord
30 Denticulate ligament
31 Dura mater
32 Sympathetic trunk
33 Common carotid artery
34 Vagus nerve
35 Internal carotid artery
36 Superior cervical sympathetic ganglion
37 Hypoglossal nerve

Figure 3-4 *Brainstem and upper part of the spinal cord, from behind*

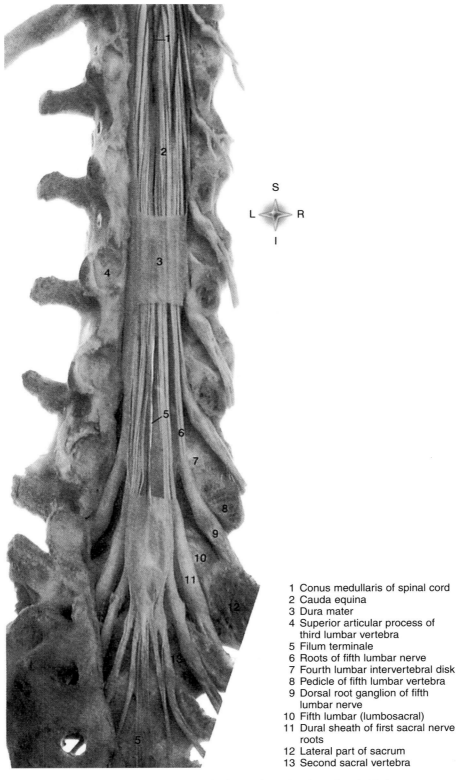

1 Conus medullaris of spinal cord
2 Cauda equina
3 Dura mater
4 Superior articular process of
  third lumbar vertebra
5 Filum terminale
6 Roots of fifth lumbar nerve
7 Fourth lumbar intervertebral disk
8 Pedicle of fifth lumbar vertebra
9 Dorsal root ganglion of fifth
  lumbar nerve
10 Fifth lumbar (lumbosacral)
11 Dural sheath of first sacral nerve
   roots
12 Lateral part of sacrum
13 Second sacral vertebra

Figure 3-5 *Vertebral column, lumbar and sacral regions, from behind*

1 Lateral cord
2 Posterior cord
3 Medial cord
4 Pectoralis minor and lateral pectoral nerve
5 Musculocutaneous nerve
6 Axillary nerve
7 Lateral root of median nerve
8 Radial nerve
9 Medial root of median nerve
10 Upper subscapular nerves
11 Thoracodorsal nerve
12 Lower subscapular nerve
13 Medial cutaneous nerve of arm
14 Ulnar nerve
15 Medial cutaneous nerve of forearm
16 Intercostobrachial nerve
17 Subscapularis
18 Teres major
19 Latissimus dorsi
20 Long head of triceps
21 Lateral head of triceps
22 Medial head of triceps
23 Radial nerve branches to triceps
24 Median nerve
25 Coracobrachialis
26 Biceps
27 Deltoid

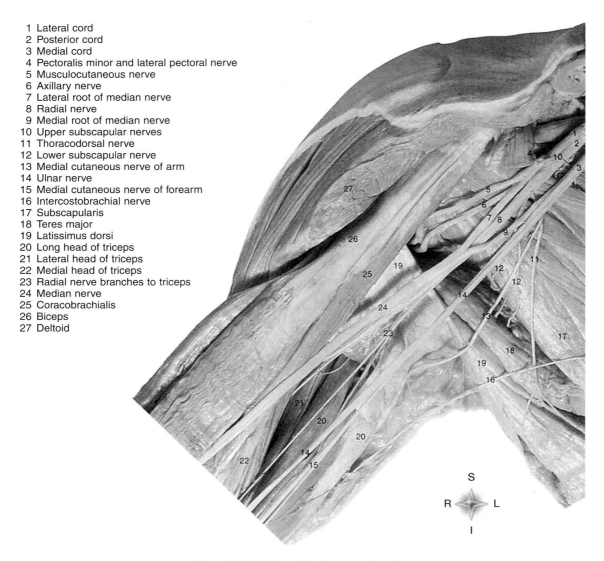

Figure 3-6 *Right brachial plexus and branches*

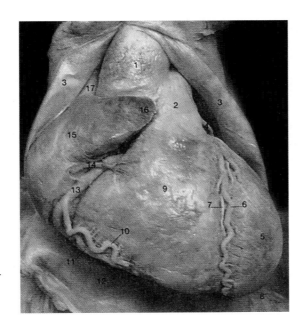

1 Ascending aorta
2 Pulmonary trunk
3 Serous pericardium overlying fibrous pericardium (turned laterally)
4 Auricle of left atrium
5 Left ventricle
6 Anterior interventricular branch of left coronary artery
7 Great cardiac vein
8 Diaphragm
9 Right ventricle
10 Marginal branch of right coronary artery
11 Small cardiac vein
12 Pericardium fused with tendon of diaphragm
13 Right coronary artery
14 Anterior cardiac vein
15 Right atrium
16 Auricle of right atrium
17 Superior vena cava

S
R L
I

Figure 3-7 *Heart and pericardium, from the front*

S
R L
I

1 Arch of cricoid cartilage
2 Isthmus   } of thyroid
3 Lateral lobe } gland
4 Trachea
5 Inferior thyroid veins
6 Left common carotid artery
7 Left vagus nerve
8 Internal jugular vein
9 Subclavian vein
10 Thoracic duct
11 Internal thoracic vein
12 Internal thoracic artery
13 Phrenic nerve
14 Parietal pleura (cut edge) over lung
15 Left brachiocephalic vein
16 A thymic artery
17 Thymic veins
18 Thymus
19 Superior vena cava
20 Right brachiocephalic vein
21 First rib
22 Brachiocephalic trunk
23 Right common carotid artery
24 Right subclavian artery
25 Right recurrent laryngeal nerve
26 Right vagus nerve
27 Unusual cervical tributary of 20
28 Vertebral vein
29 Thyrocervical trunk
30 Suprascapular artery
31 Scalenus anterior
32 Upper trunk of brachial plexus
33 Superficial cervical artery
34 Ascending cervical artery
35 Inferior thyroid artery
36 Sympathetic trunk

Figure 3-8 *Thoracic inlet and mediastinum, from the front.*

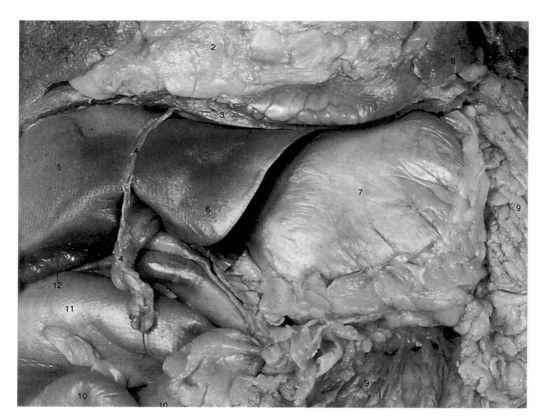

1 Inferior lobe of right lung
2 Pericardial fat
3 Diaphragm
4 Falciform ligament
5 Right lobe of liver
6 Left lobe of liver
7 Stomach
8 Inferior lobe of left lung
9 Greater omentum
10 Small intestine
11 Transverse colon
12 Gallbladder

Figure 3-9 *Upper abdominal viscera, from the front.*

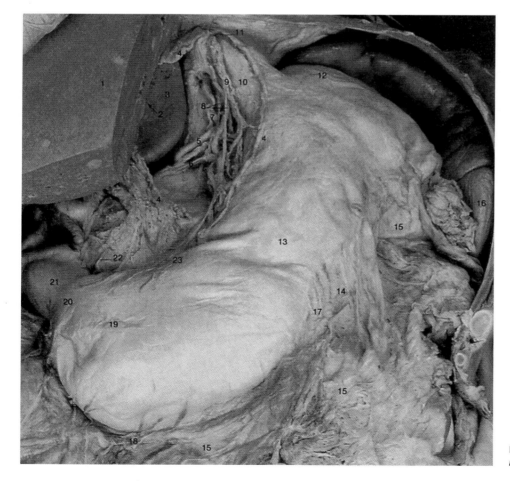

1 Right lobe of liver
2 Fissure of ligamentum venosum
3 Caudate lobe of liver
4 Lesser omentum (cut edge)
5 Left gastric artery
6 Left gastric vein
7 Posterior vagal trunk
8 Esophageal branches of left gastric vessels
9 Anterior vagal trunk
10 Esophagus
11 Esophageal opening in diaphragm
12 Fundus ⎫
13 Body   ⎬ of stomach
14 Greater curvature ⎭
15 Greater omentum
16 Lower end of spleen
17 Branches of left gastroepiploic vessels
18 Right gastroepiploic vessels and branches
19 Pyloric part of stomach
20 Pylorus
21 Superior (first) part of duodenum
22 Right gastric artery
23 Lesser curvature

Figure 3-10 *Stomach, with vessels and vagus nerves, from the front.*

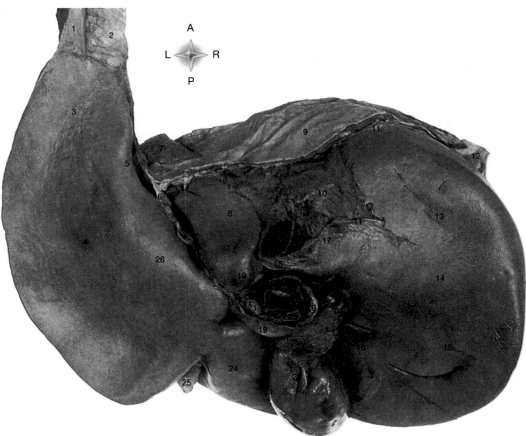

1 Left triangular ligament
2 Diaphragm
3 Left lobe
4 Gastric impression
5 Esophageal groove
6 Lesser omentum in fissure for ligamentum venosum
7 Inferior vena cava
8 Caudate lobe
9 Diaphragm on part of bare area
10 Bare area
11 Inferior layer of coronary ligament
12 Right triangular ligament
13 Renal impression
14 Right lobe
15 Colic impression
16 Duodenal impression
17 Suprarenal impression
18 Caudate process
19 Right free margin of lesser omentum in porta hepatis
20 Portal vein
21 Hepatic artery
22 Common hepatic duct
23 Gallbladder
24 Quadrate lobe
25 Ligamentum teres and falciform ligament in fissure for legamentum teres
26 Omental tuberosity

Figure 3-11 *Liver, from above and behind.*

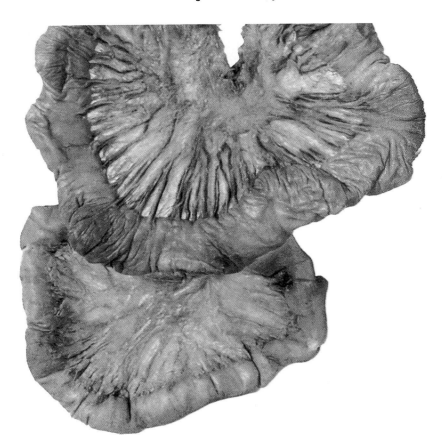

Figure 3-12 *Small Intestine.*
Coil of typical jejunum, coil of typical ileum.

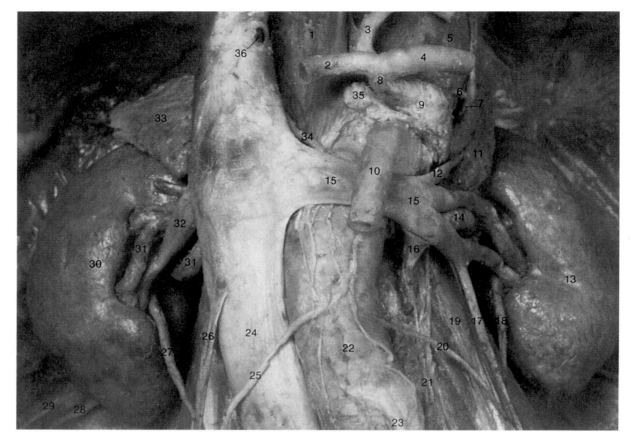

Figure 3-13 *Kidneys and suprarenal glands.*

1 Right crus of diaphragm
2 Common hepatic artery
3 Left gastric artery
4 Splenic artery
5 Left crus of diaphragm
6 Left inferior phrenic arter
7 Left inferior phrenic vein
8 Celiac trunk
9 Left celiac ganglion
10 Superior mesenteric artery
11 Left suprarenal gland
12 Left suprarenal vein
13 Left kidney
14 Left renal artery
15 Left renal vein
16 Lumbar tributary of renal vein
17 Left gonadal vein
18 Left ureter

19 Left psoas major
20 Left gonadal artery
21 Left sympathetic trunk
22 Abdominal aorta and aortic plexus
23 Inferior mesenteric artery
24 Inferior vena cava
25 Right gonadal artery
26 Right gonadal vein
27 Right ureter
28 Right ilio-inguinal nerve
29 Right iliohypogastric nerve
30 Right kidney
31 Right renal artery
32 Right renal vein
33 Right suprarenal gland
34 Right inferior phrenic artery
35 Right celiac ganglion
36 A hepatic vein

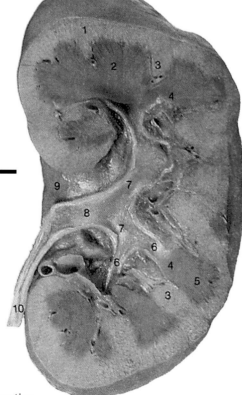

1 Cortex
2 Medulla
3 Renal column
4 Renal papilla
5 Medullary pyramid
6 Minor calyx
7 Major calyx
8 Renal pelvis
9 Hilum
10 Ureter

Figure 3-14 *Kidney.* Internal structure in longitudinal section.

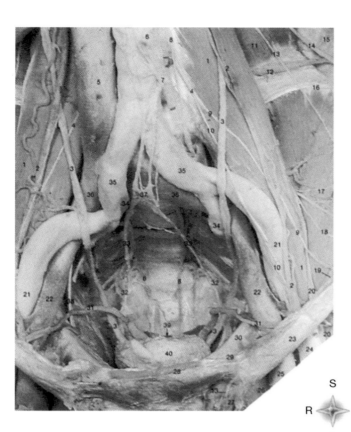

1 Psoas major
2 Testicular vessels
3 Ureter
4 Genitofemoral nerve
5 Inferior vena cava
6 Aorta and aortic plexus
7 Inferior mesenteric artery and plexus
8 Sympathetic trunk and ganglia
9 Femoral ⎱ branch of
10 Genital ⎰ genitofemoral nerve
11 Quadratus lumborum
12 Fourth lumbar artery
13 Ilio-inguinal nerve
14 Iliohypogastric nerve
15 Lumbar part of thoracolumbar fascia
16 Iliolumbar ligament
17 Iliacus and branches from femoral nerve and iliolumbar artery
18 Lateral femoral cutaneous nerve arising from femoral nerve
19 Deep circumflex iliac artery
20 Femoral nerve
21 External iliac artery
22 External iliac vein
23 Inguinal ligament
24 Femoral artery
25 Femoral vein
26 Position of femoral canal
27 Spermatic cord
28 Rectus abdominis
29 Lacunar ligament
30 Pectineal ligament
31 Ductus deferens
32 Inferior hypogastric (pelvic) plexus and pelvic splanchnic nerves
33 Hypogastric nerve
34 Internal iliac artery
35 Common iliac artery
36 Common iliac vein
37 Superior hypogastric plexus
38 Obturator nerve and vessels
39 Rectum (cut edge)
40 Bladder

Figure 3-15 *Posterior abdominal and pelvic walls.*

1 Rectus abdominis
2 Extraperitoneal fat
3 Sigmoid colon
4 Promontory of sacrum
5 Rectum
6 Coccyx
7 Anococcygeal body
8 External anal sphincter
9 Anal canal with anal columns of mucous membrane
10 Perineal body
11 Ductus deferens
12 Epididymis
13 Testis
14 Spongy part of urethra and corpus spongiosum
15 Corpus cavernosum
16 Bulbospongiosus
17 Perineal membrane
18 Sphincter urethrae
19 Membranous part of urethra
20 Pubic symphysis
21 Prostate
22 Prostatic part of urethra
23 Seminal colliculus
24 Bristle in ejaculatory duct
25 Internal urethral orifice
26 Bladder
27 Bristle passing up into right ureteral orifice
28 Rectovesical pouch
29 Puborectalis fibers of levator ani

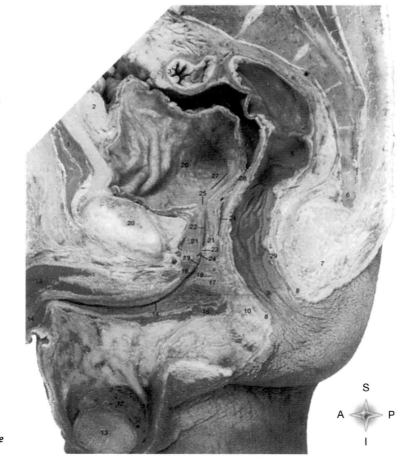

Figure 3-16 *Right half of a midline sagittal section of the male pelvis.*

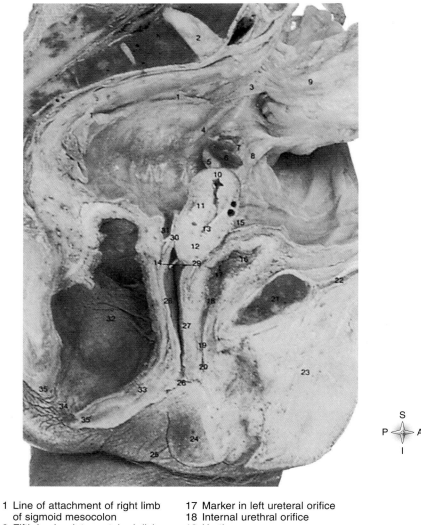

1 Line of attachment of right limb
   of sigmoid mesocolon
2 Fifth lumbar intervertebral disk
3 Apex of sigmoid mesocolon
4 Ureter underlying peritoneum
5 Ovary
6 Uterine tube
7 Suspensory ligament of ovary
   containing ovarian vessels
8 Left limb of sigmoid mesocolon
   overlying external iliac vessels
9 Sigmoid colon (reflected to left
   and upwards)
10 Fundus ⎫
11 Body   ⎬ of uterus
12 Cervix ⎭
13 Marker in internal os
14 Marker in external os
15 Vesico-uterine pouch
16 Bladder

17 Marker in left ureteral orifice
18 Internal urethral orifice
19 Urethra
20 External urethral orifice
21 Pubic symphysis
22 Rectus abdominis (turned
   forwards)
23 Fat of mons pubis
24 Labium minus
25 Labium majus
26 Vestibule   ⎫
27 Anterior wall ⎪
28 Posterior wall ⎬ of vagina
29 Anterior fornix ⎪
30 Posterior fornix⎭
31 Recto-uterine pouch
32 Rectum
33 Perineal body
34 Anal canal
35 External anal sphincter

Figure 3-17 *Left half of a midline sagittal section of the female pelvis.*

1 Ascending aorta
2 Pulmonary trunk and sinuses above pulmonary valve cusps
3 Anterior interventricular branch of left coronary artery and great cardiac vein
4 Vessels of interventricular septum
5 Middle cardiac vein and posterior interventricular branch of right coronary artery
6 Marginal branch of right coronary artery and small cardiac vein
7 Coronary sinus
8 Right coronary artery
9 Anterior cardiac vein

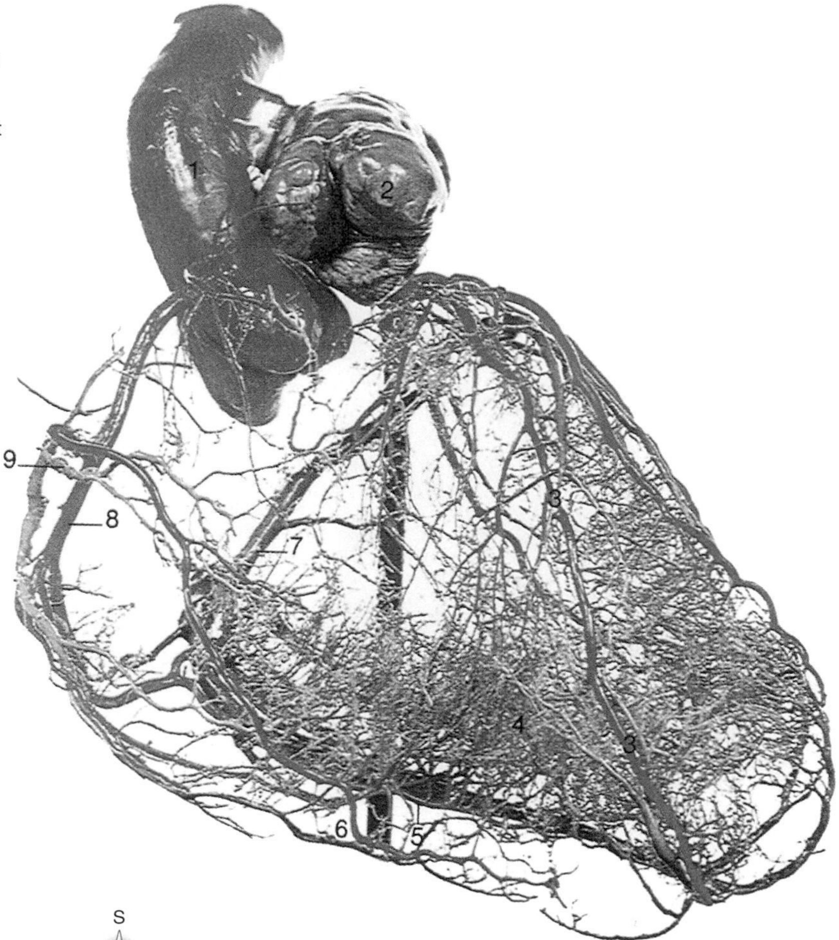

Figure 3-18 *Cast of the cardiac vessels, from the front*

1 Azygos vein
2 Superior vena cava
3 Ascending aorta
4 Arch of aorta
5 Brachiocephalic trunk
6 Left common carotid artery
7 Left subclavian artery
8 Pulmonary trunk
9 Left ventricle
10 Anterior interventricular branch of left coronary artery and great cardiac vein
11 Right ventricle
12 Marginal branch of right coronary artery and small cardiac vein
13 Right coronary artery
14 Anterior cardiac vein
15 Right atrium
16 Auricle of right atrium

Figure 3-19 *Cast of the heart and great vessels, from the front*

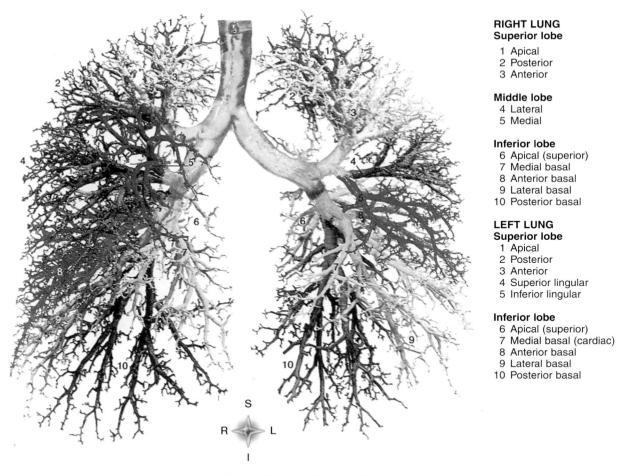

RIGHT LUNG
Superior lobe

1 Apical
2 Posterior
3 Anterior

Middle lobe
4 Lateral
5 Medial

Inferior lobe
6 Apical (superior)
7 Medial basal
8 Anterior basal
9 Lateral basal
10 Posterior basal

LEFT LUNG
Superior lobe

1 Apical
2 Posterior
3 Anterior
4 Superior lingular
5 Inferior lingular

Inferior lobe
6 Apical (superior)
7 Medial basal (cardiac)
8 Anterior basal
9 Lateral basal
10 Posterior basal

Figure 3-20 *Cast of the bronchial tree.*

1 Right branch of portal vein and hepatic artery
   and right hepatic duct
2 Gallbladder
3 Bile duct
4 Hepatic artery
5 Portal vein
6 Left branch of portal vein and hepatic artery
   and left hepatic duct
7 Left gastric artery
8 Left gastric vein
9 Splenic artery
10 Splenic vein
11 Short gastric vessels
12 Left gastroepiploic vessels
13 Vessels of left kidney
14 Pancreatic duct
15 Duodenojejunal flexure
16 Superior mesenteric artery
17 Superior mesenteric vein
18 Horizontal (third) part of duodenum
19 Right gastroepiploic vessels
20 Pyloric canal
21 Pylorus
22 Superior (first) part of duodenum
23 Right gastric vessels
24 Branches of superior and inferior pancreatico-
   duodenal vessels
25 Descending (second) part of duodenum
26 Vessels of right kidney

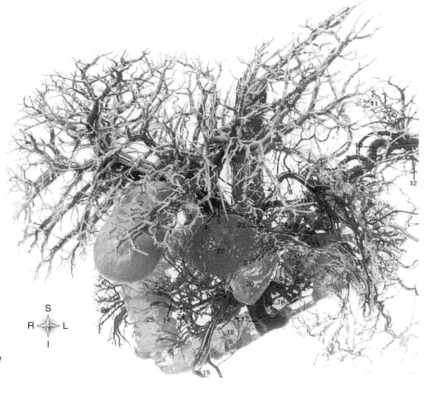

Figure 3-21 *Cast of the duodenum, liver, biliary tract, and associated vessels, from the front*

1 Right renal vein	7 Left renal vein
2 Right suprarenal vein	8 Left suprarenal veins
3 Inferior vena cava	9 Left renal artery
4 Aorta	10 Accessory renal
5 Celiac trunk	arteries
6 Superior mesenteric	11 Right renal artery
artery	

Figure 3-22 *Cast of the kidneys and great vessels, from the front*

Cross-sectional Anatomy

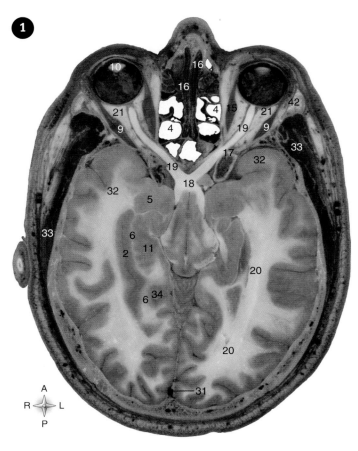

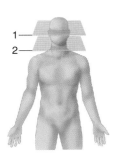

1 Arytenoid cartilage
2 Claustrum
3 Common carotid artery
4 Ethmoidal air cells
5 Head of caudate nucleus
6 Internal capsule of cerebrum
7 Internal jugular vein
8 Lamina of vertebra
9 Lateral rectus muscle
10 Lens
11 Lentiform nucleus
12 Levator scapulae muscle
13 Ligamentum nuchae
14 Longus colli muscle
15 Medial rectus muscle
16 Nasal cavity
17 Optic canal
18 Optic chiasma
19 Optic nerve
20 Optic radiation
21 Orbital fat
22 Piriform fossa, pharynx
23 Platysma muscle
24 Scalenus anterior muscle
25 Scalenus medius and scalenus posterior
26 Semispinalis capitis muscle
27 Spinal cord
28 Spinalis muscle
29 Splenius capitis muscle
30 Sternocleidomastoid muscle
31 Superior sagittal sinus
32 Temporal lobe, cerebrum
33 Temporalis muscle
34 Thalamus
35 Thyroid cartilage
36 Thyroid gland, lateral lobe
37 Trapezius muscle
38 Vertebral artery in transverse foramen
39 Vertebral body
40 Vertebral canal
41 Vocal cord
42 Zygomatic bone

Figure 4-1 *Head and neck* (cross-section at level of optic chiasma, inferior view)

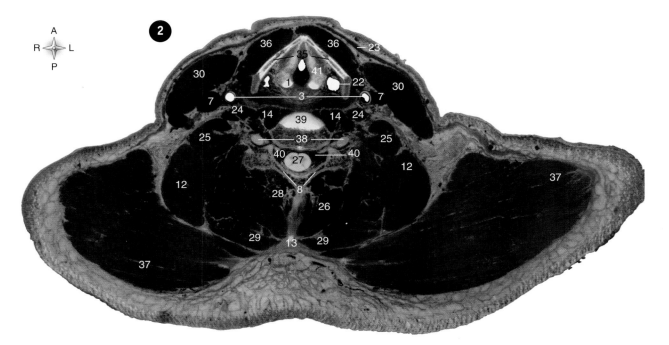

Figure 4-2 *Head and neck* (cross-section at level of vocal cords, inferior view)

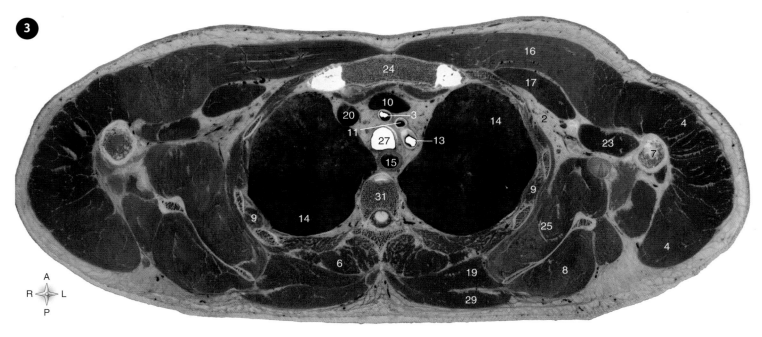

Figure 4-3 *Thorax* (cross-section at T2 vertebral level, inferior view)

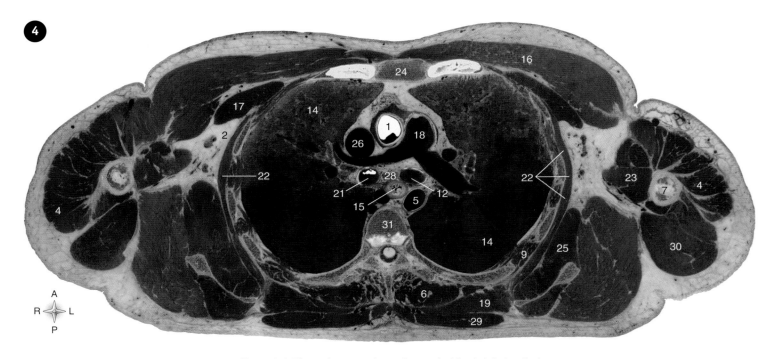

Figure 4-4 *Thorax* (cross-section at T4 vertebral level, inferior view)

1 Ascending aorta	12 Left main bronchus	23 Short head of biceps brachii
2 Axillary fat with brachial plexus	13 Left subclavian artery	24 Sternal marrow
3 Brachiocephalic artery	14 Lung	25 Subscapularis muscle
4 Deltoid muscle	15 Esophagus	26 Superior vena cava
5 Descending aorta	16 Pectoralis major muscle	27 Trachea
6 Erector spinae muscle	17 Pectoralis minor muscle	28 Tracheobronchial lymph
7 Humerus	18 Pulmonary trunk	29 Trapezius muscle
8 Infraspinatus muscle	19 Rhomboid major muscle	30 Triceps muscle
9 Intercostal muscles	20 Right brachiocephalic vein	31 Vertebral body
10 Left braciocephalic vein	21 Right main bronchus	
11 Left common carotid artery	22 Serratus anterior muscle	

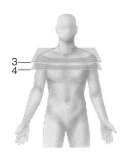

1 Aorta
2 Body of pancreas
3 Descending colon
4 Diaphragm
5 Duodenum
6 Erector spinae muscle
7 External oblique muscle
8 Gall bladder
9 Head of pancreas
10 Inferior vena cava
11 Intercostal muscle
12 Intervertebral disc
13 Kidney
14 Latissimus dorsi muscle
15 Left crus of diaphragm
16 Left renal vein
17 Linea alba
18 Linea semilunaris
19 Liver
20 Perirenal fat
21 Portal vein
22 Psoas muscle
23 Quadratus abdominis muscle
24 Rectus abdominis muscle
25 Rib
26 Right crus of diaphragm
27 Small intestine
28 Spinal cord
29 Spleen
30 Splenic artery and vein
31 Stomach
32 Superior mesenteric vessels
33 Tail of pancreas
34 Transverse colon
35 Vertebral body

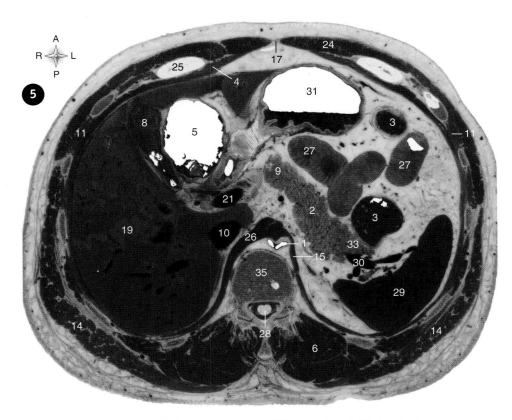

Figure 4-5 *Abdomen* (cross-section at L1 vertebral level, inferior view)

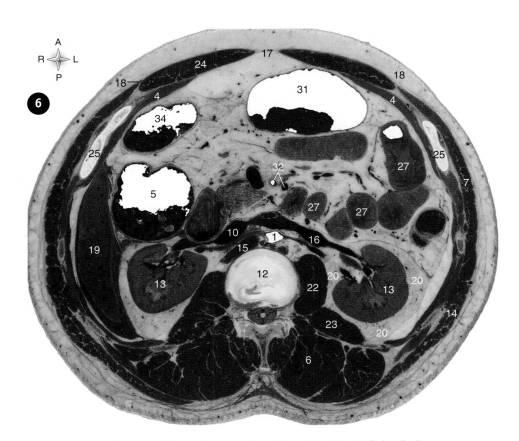

Figure 4-6 *Abdomen* (cross-section at L2 vertebral level, inferior view)

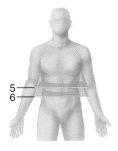

1 Adductor brevis muscle
2 Adductor longus muscle
3 Adductor magnus muscle
4 Anal canal
5 Bladder
6 Bulb of penis
7 Coccygeus part of levator ani muscle
8 Coccyx
9 Crus of penis
10 Femoral artery
11 Femoral nerve
12 Femoral vein
13 Femur
14 Gluteus maximus muscle
15 Gluteus minimus muscle
16 Great saphenous vein
17 Hamstring origin
18 Head of femur
19 Ischiocavernosus
20 Ischial tuberosity
21 Ischioanal fossa
22 Ischium
23 Levator ani muscle
24 Ligament of head of femur
25 Iliopsoas muscle
26 Iliotibial tract
27 Obturator externus muscle
28 Obturator internus muscle
29 Pectineus muscle
30 Quadratus femoris muscle
31 Rectum
32 Rectus abdominis muscle
33 Rectus femoris muscle
34 Sartorius muscle
35 Sciatic nerve
36 Seminal vesicles
37 Spermatic cord
38 Tensor fasciae latae muscle
39 Vastus intermedius muscle
40 Vastus lateralis muscle

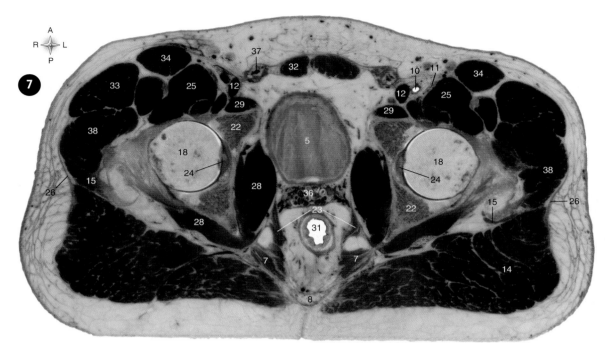

Figure 4-7 *Pelvic Region* (cross-section at level of the hip joint in a male pelvis, inferior view)

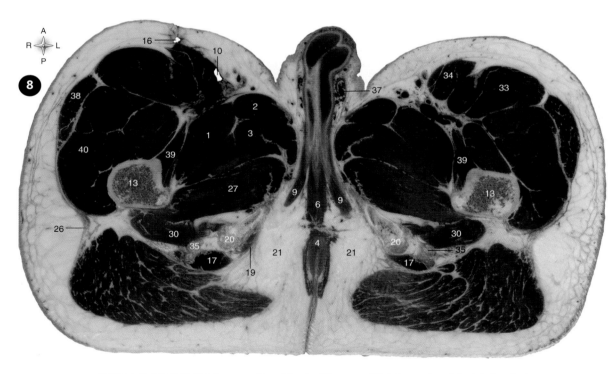

Figure 4-8 *Pelvic Region* (cross-section at level of the upper thigh in a male pelvis, inferior view)

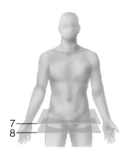

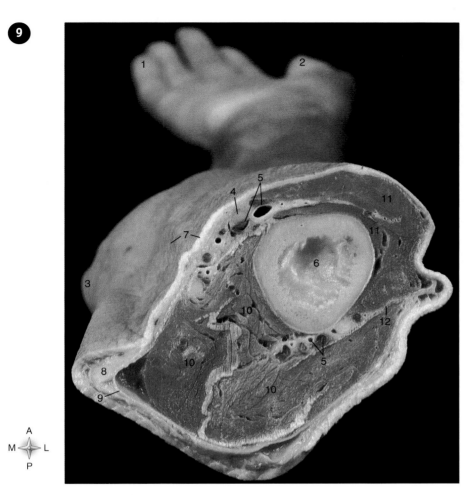

1. Digit 5 (little finger)
2. Digit 1 (thumb)
3. Medial epicondyle (surface bump)
4. Nerve
5. Blood vessels
6. Humerus
7. Skin
8. Superficial fascia
9. Deep fascia
10. Muscles of the posterior compartment
11. Muscles of the anterior compartment
12. Lateral intermuscular septum

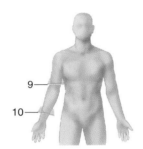

Figure 4-9 *Upper Arm.* Cross section proximal to the elbow.

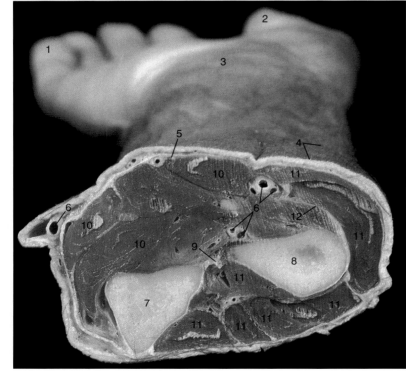

1. Digit 5 (little finger)
2. Digit 1 (thumb)
3. Carpus (wrist)
4. Skin
5. Deep fascia
6. Blood vessels
7. Ulna
8. Radius
9. Interosseus ligament
10. Muscles of the anterior compartment
11. Muscles of the posterior compartment
12. Intermuscular septum

Figure 4-10 *Lower arm.* Cross section distal to the elbow.

11

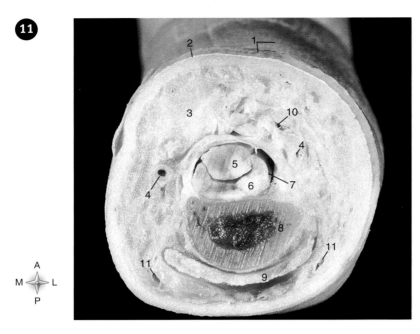

1. Epidermis
2. Dermis
3. Superficial fascia
4. Digital artery
5. Tendon (flexor digitorum superficialis)
6. Tendon (flexor digitorum profundis)
7. Tendon sheath
8. Proximal phalanx
9. Tendon (extensor expansion)
10. Digital nerve
11. Digital vein

Figure 4-11 *Second digit (index finger).* Cross section at the proximal phalanx.

12

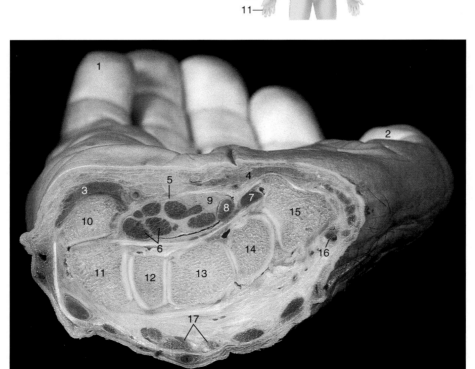

1. Digit 5 (little finger)
2. Digit 1 (thumb)
3. Hypothenar muscles
4. Thenar muscles
5. Tendon sheath (of carpal tunnel)
6. Tendons (digital flexor)
7. Flexor carpi radialis
8. Flexor pollicis longus
9. Median nerve
10. Pisiform
11. Triquetral
12. Hamate
13. Capitate
14. Trapezoid
15. Trapezium
16. Radial artery
17. Tendons (digital extensor)

Figure 4-12 *Carpus (wrist).* Cross section showing the carpal tunnel.

13

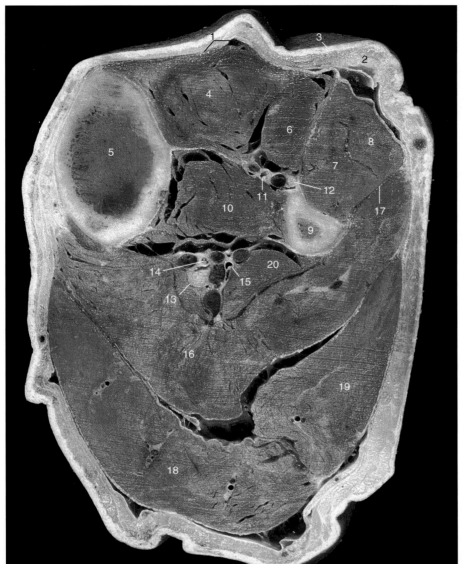

1. Deep fascia
2. Superficial fascia
3. Skin
4. Tibialis anterior
5. Tibia
6. Extensor digitorum longus
7. Peroneus brevis
8. Peroneus longus
9. Fibula
10. Tibialis posterior
11. Anterior tibial artery
12. Deep peroneal nerve
13. Tibial nerve
14. Posterior tibial artery
15. Peroneal artery
16. Soleus
17. Posterior peroneal intermuscular septum
18. Gastrocnemius (medial head)
19. Gastrocnemius (lateral head)
20. Flexor hallucis longus

Figure 4-13 *Leg.* Cross section showing bones and muscles below the knee.

14

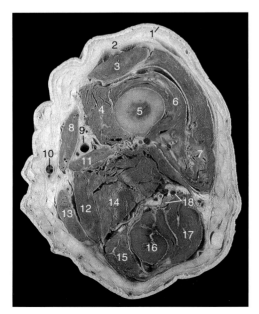

1. Skin
2. Superficial fascia
3. Rectus femoris
4. Vastus medialis
5. Femur
6. Vastus intermedius
7. Vastus lateralis
8. Sartorius
9. Femoral artery
10. Great saphenous vein
11. Adductor longus
12. Adductor brevis
13. Gracilis
14. Adductor magnus
15. Semimembranosus
16. Semitendinosus
17. Biceps femoris
18. Branches of sciatic nerve

Figure 4-14 *Thigh.* Cross section showing major muscles above the knee.

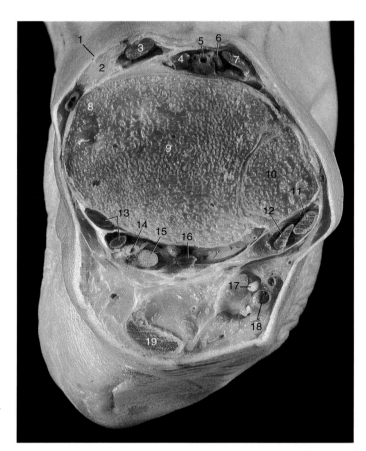

1. Skin
2. Superficial fascia
3. Tendon (tibialis anterior)
4. Tendon (extensor hallucis longus)
5. Anterior tibial artery
6. Deep peroneal nerve
7. Tendon (extensor digitorum longus)
8. Great saphenous vein
9. Tibia
10. Lateral malleolus of fibula
11. Tendon (peroneus longus)
12. Tendon (peroneus brevis)
13. Tendons (tibialis posterior, flexor digitorum longus)
14. Posterior tibial artery
15. Posterior tibial nerve
16. Tendon (flexor hallucis longus)
17. Sural nerve
18. Short saphenous vein
19 Tendon (calcaenal or Achilles)

Figure 4-15 *Lower leg.* Cross section just above the ankle joint cavity, showing relations of structures.

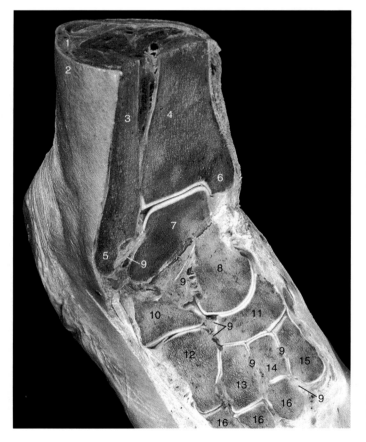

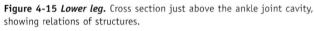

1. Superficial fascia
2. Skin
3. Fibula
4. Tibia
5. Lateral malleolus of fibula
6. Medial malleolus of tibia
7. Trochlea of talus
8. Head of talus
9. Interosseus ligaments
10. Calcaneous
11. Navicular
12. Cuboid
13. Third cuneiform
14. Second cuneiform
15. First cuneiform
16. Base of metatarsal

Figure 4-16 *Ankle and foot.* Combined cross section through anterior part of tarsal region and frontal (coronal) section through the lower leg and tarsal region.

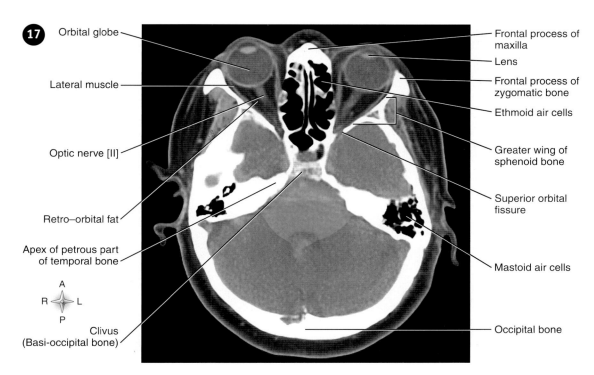

17 Orbital globe

Lateral muscle

Optic nerve [II]

Retro—orbital fat

Apex of petrous part
of temporal bone

A
R ✛ L
P

Clivus
(Basi-occipital bone)

Frontal process of
maxilla

Lens

Frontal process of
zygomatic bone

Ethmoid air cells

Greater wing of
sphenoid bone

Superior orbital
fissure

Mastoid air cells

Occipital bone

Figure 4-17 *Head.* Computerized tomography (CT) scan showing a cross section of the head at the level of the eye orbit.

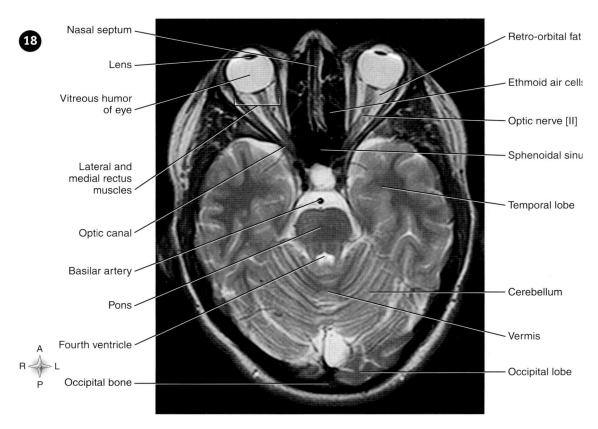

18 Nasal septum

Lens

Vitreous humor
of eye

Lateral and
medial rectus
muscles

Optic canal

Basilar artery

Pons

Fourth ventricle

A
R ✛ L
P

Occipital bone

Retro-orbital fat

Ethmoid air cells

Optic nerve [II]

Sphenoidal sinu

Temporal lobe

Cerebellum

Vermis

Occipital lobe

Figure 4-18 *Head.* Magnetic resonance imaging (MRI) scan showing a cross section of the head at the level of the eye orbit. Compare the similar cross-section above (Figure 4-17) and note that visualization of individual structures varies depending on the imaging technology used to produce the image. (See the boxed essay on p. 17-18 of Anatomy & Physiology.)

19 Sternocleidomastoid muscle

Pectoralis major muscle

Pectoralis minor muscle

Latissimus dorsi muscle

Right brachiocephalic vein

Subscapularis muscle

Serratus anterior muscle

Manubrium

Medial end of clavicle

Right brachiocephalic artery

Left brachiocephalic vein

Left common carotid artery

Left subclavian artery

Trachea

Infraspinatus muscle

Esophagus

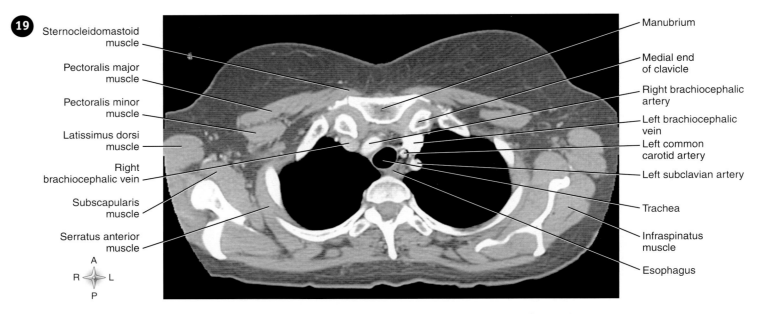

Figure 4-19 *Thorax.* CT scan showing a cross section of the chest wall and structures of the mediastinum.

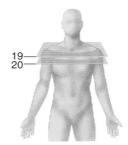

20 Internal thoracic artery and vein

Ascending aorta

Superior vena cava

Right pulmonary artery

Thoracic vertebral body

Trapezius muscle

Sternum

Main pulmonary artery (trunk)

Left lung

Superior pulmonary vein

Left descending interlobar pulmonary artery

Descending aorta

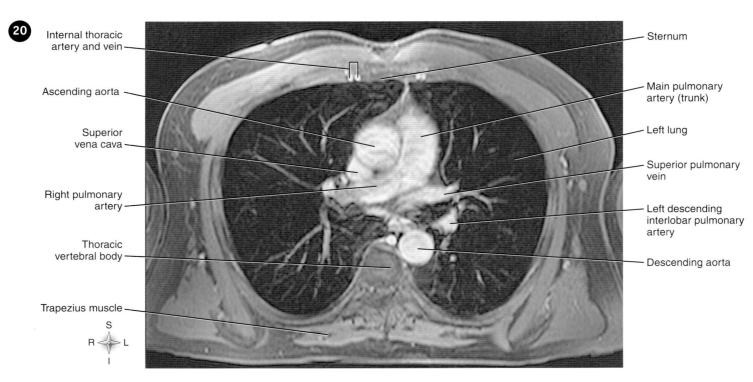

Figure 4-20 *Thorax.* MRI scan showing a cross section of the chest.

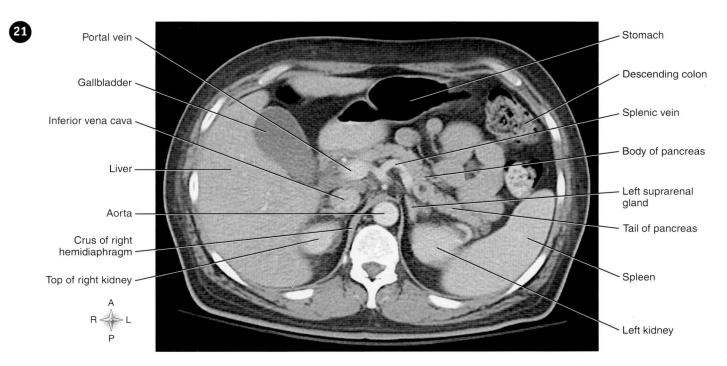

21

Portal vein

Gallbladder

Inferior vena cava

Liver

Aorta

Crus of right hemidiaphragm

Top of right kidney

Stomach

Descending colon

Splenic vein

Body of pancreas

Left suprarenal gland

Tail of pancreas

Spleen

Left kidney

A
R — L
P

Figure 4-21 *Abdomen.* CT scan showing a cross section of the upper abdominal wall and internal abdominal organs.

21
22

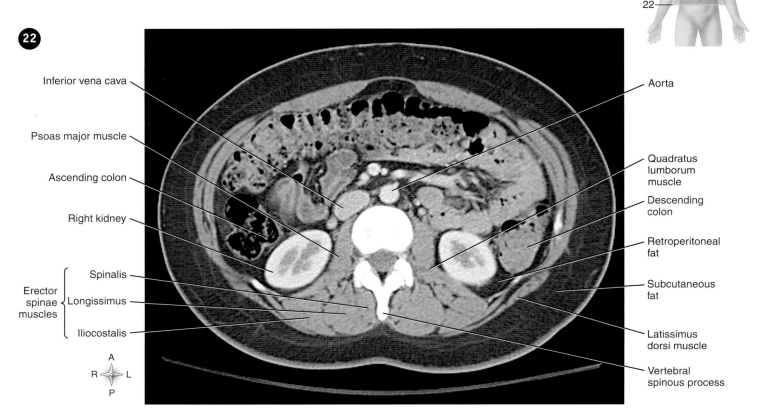

22

Inferior vena cava

Psoas major muscle

Ascending colon

Right kidney

Erector spinae muscles
  Spinalis
  Longissimus
  Iliocostalis

Aorta

Quadratus lumborum muscle

Descending colon

Retroperitoneal fat

Subcutaneous fat

Latissimus dorsi muscle

Vertebral spinous process

A
R — L
P

Figure 4-22 *Abdomen.* CT scan showing a cross section of the lower abdominal contents and wall. Note the clear definition of the muscles of the back.

23

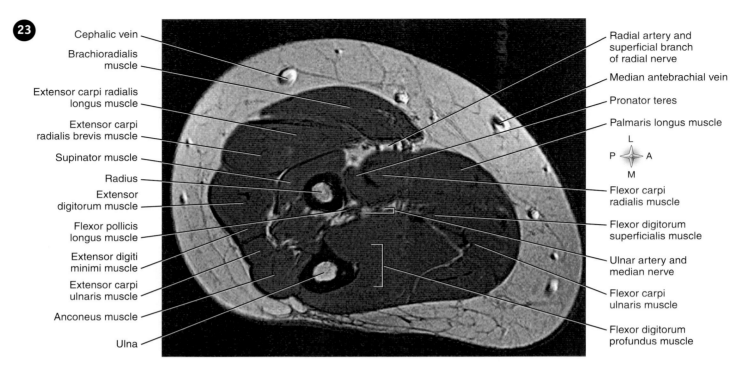

Cephalic vein

Brachioradialis muscle

Extensor carpi radialis longus muscle

Extensor carpi radialis brevis muscle

Supinator muscle

Radius

Extensor digitorum muscle

Flexor pollicis longus muscle

Extensor digiti minimi muscle

Extensor carpi ulnaris muscle

Anconeus muscle

Ulna

Radial artery and superficial branch of radial nerve

Median antebrachial vein

Pronator teres

Palmaris longus muscle

L

P A

M

Flexor carpi radialis muscle

Flexor digitorum superficialis muscle

Ulnar artery and median nerve

Flexor carpi ulnaris muscle

Flexor digitorum profundus muscle

Figure 4-23 *Forearm.* MRI scan showing a cross section of the antebrachial region of the upper limb.

24

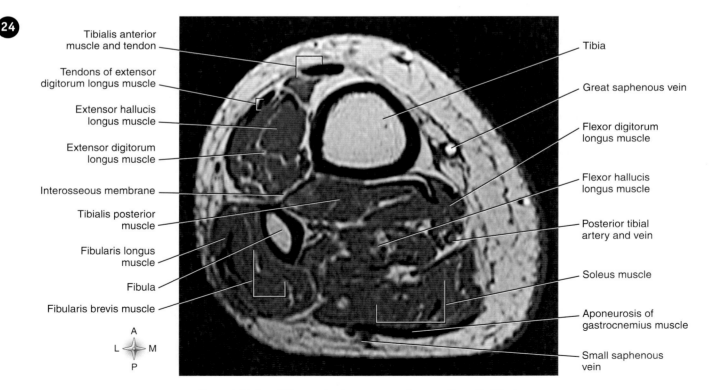

Tibialis anterior muscle and tendon

Tendons of extensor digitorum longus muscle

Extensor hallucis longus muscle

Extensor digitorum longus muscle

Interosseous membrane

Tibialis posterior muscle

Fibularis longus muscle

Fibula

Fibularis brevis muscle

A

L M

P

Tibia

Great saphenous vein

Flexor digitorum longus muscle

Flexor hallucis longus muscle

Posterior tibial artery and vein

Soleus muscle

Aponeurosis of gastrocnemius muscle

Small saphenous vein

Figure 4-24 *Leg.* MRI scan showing a cross section near the calf of the leg.

Histology

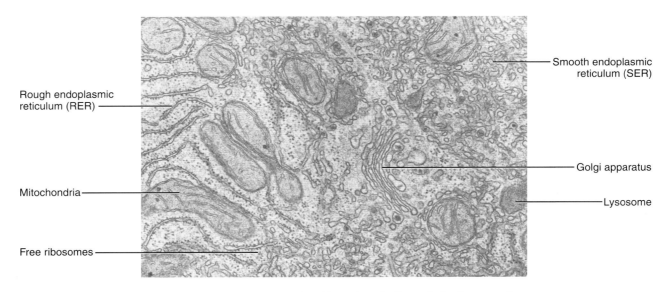

Rough endoplasmic reticulum (RER)

Mitochondria

Free ribosomes

Smooth endoplasmic reticulum (SER)

Golgi apparatus

Lysosome

Figure 5-1 *Electron micrograph of a thin section of a liver cell showing organelles.*

Table 5-1   Mitosis

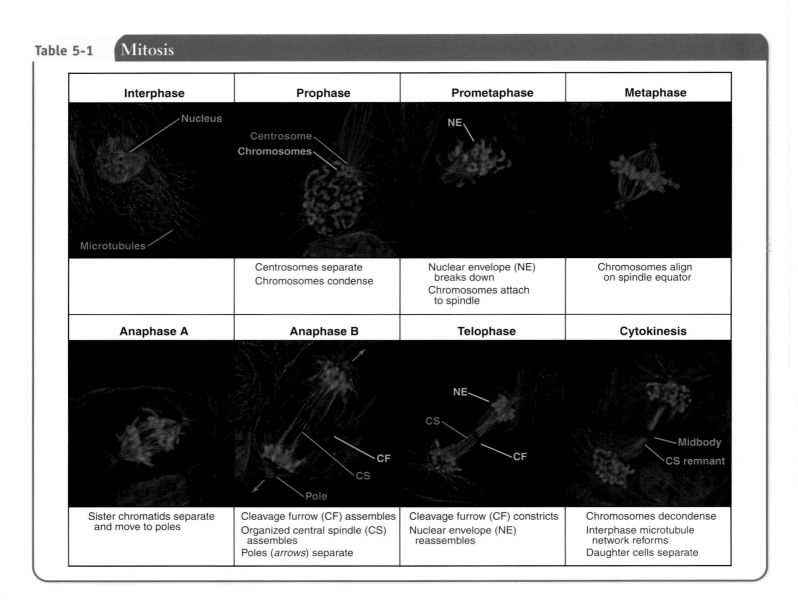

Interphase	Prophase	Prometaphase	Metaphase
	Centrosomes separate Chromosomes condense	Nuclear envelope (NE) breaks down Chromosomes attach to spindle	Chromosomes align on spindle equator

Anaphase A	Anaphase B	Telophase	Cytokinesis
Sister chromatids separate and move to poles	Cleavage furrow (CF) assembles Organized central spindle (CS) assembles Poles (*arrows*) separate	Cleavage furrow (CF) constricts Nuclear envelope (NE) reassembles	Chromosomes decondense Interphase microtubule network reforms Daughter cells separate

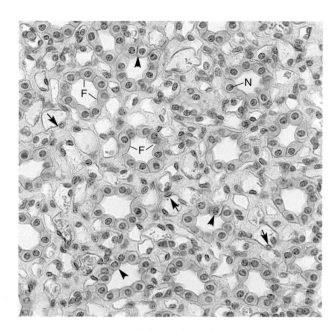

Figure 5-3 *Simple squamous epithelium* (arrows); Simple cuboidal epithelium (arrowheads) (×270) [F, free edge, N, nucleus].

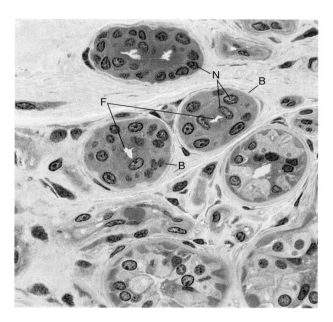

Figure 5-4 *Stratified cuboidal epithelium* (×509) [B, basement membrane; F, free edge; N, nucleus].

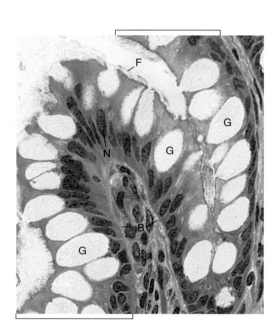

Figure 5-5 *Simple columnar epithelium with goblet cells* (×540) [G, goblet cell; N, nucleus; B, basement membrane; F, free edge].

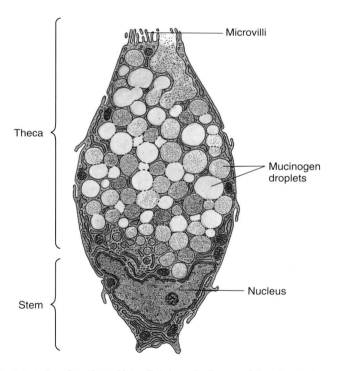

Figure 5-6 *Drawing of a goblet cell.* Schematic diagram of the ultrastructure of a goblet cell illustrating the tightly packed secretory granules of the theca.

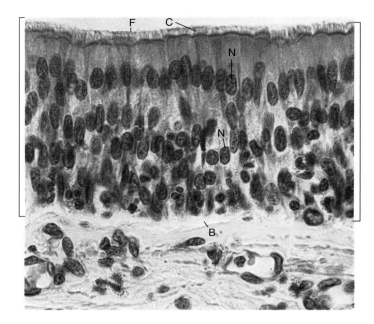

Figure 5-7 *Pseudostratified columnar epithelium* (×540) [B, basement membrane; C, cilia; F, free edge; N, nucleus].

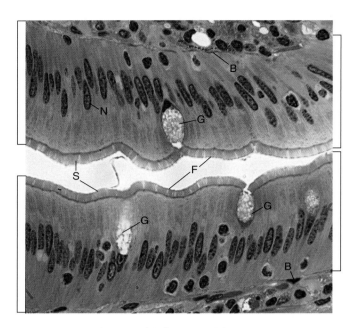

Figure 5-8 *Simple columnar epithelium* (×540) [G, goblet cell; S, striated border; N, nucleus; F, free edge; B, basement membrane].

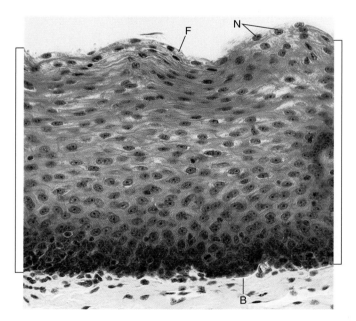

Figure 5-9 *Stratified squamous epithelium* (non-keratinized, ×509) [B, basement membrane; F, free edge; N, nucleus].

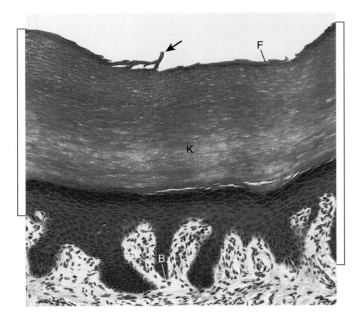

Figure 5-10 *Stratified squamous epithelium* (keratinized, ×125) [arrows, flaking off of dead cells; K, keratinized layer; F, free edge; B, basement membrane].

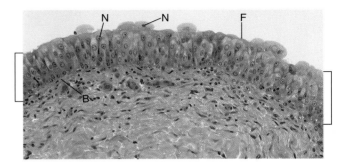

Figure 5-11 *Transitional epithelium* (×125) [B, basement membrane; F, free edge; N, nucleus].

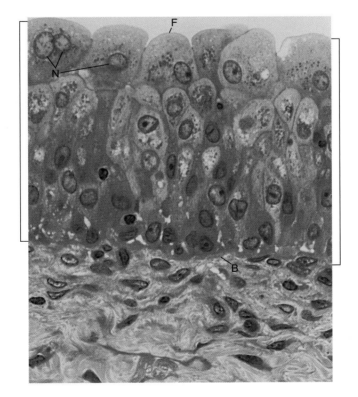

Figure 5-12 *Transitional epithelium* (×540) [B, basement membrane; F, free edge; N, nucleus].

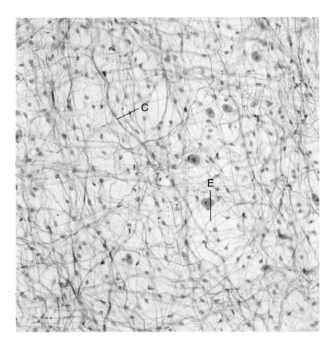

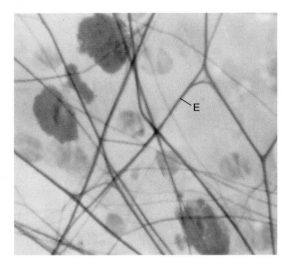

Figure 5-13 *Loose, ordinary (areolar) connective tissue* (×132) [C, collagen fiber; E, elastin fiber]

Figure 5-14 *Loose, ordinary (areolar) connective tissue* (high power) [E, elastin fiber]

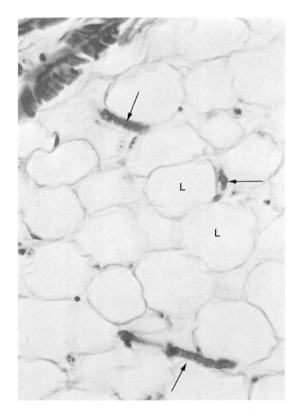

Figure 5-15 *Adipose tissue* [L, lipid-storing vesicles; arrows, blood capillaries].

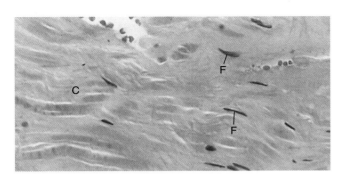

Figure 5-16 *Dense fibrous connective tissue* [C, bundles of collagen fibers; F, fibroblasts].

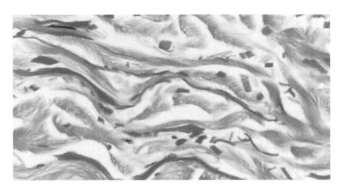

Figure 5-17 *Elastic fibrous connective tissue.*

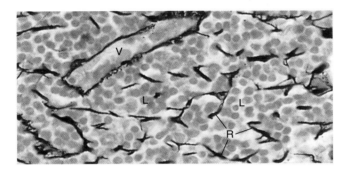

Figure 5-18 *Reticular connective tissue* [L, lymphoid cells; R, reticular fibers; V, blood vessel].

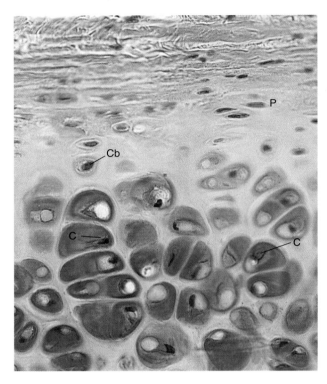

Figure 5-19 *Hyaline cartilage* (×270) [C, chondrocyte within a lacuna; Cb, chondroblast; P, perichondrium].

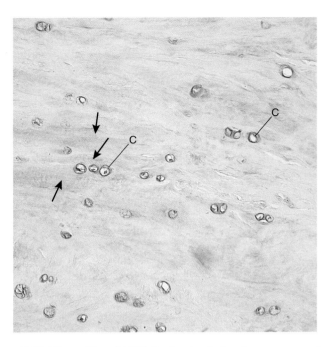

Figure 5-20 *Fibrocartilage* (×132) [C, chondrocyte in a lacuna; arrow, collagen fiber bundle].

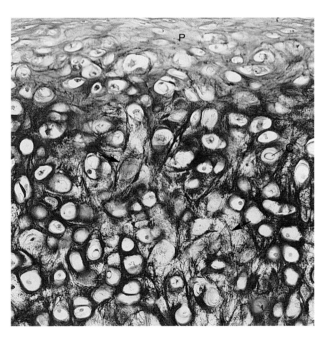

Figure 5-21 *Elastic cartilage* (×132) [P, perichondrium; C, chondrocyte in a lacuna; arrow, elastic fiber].

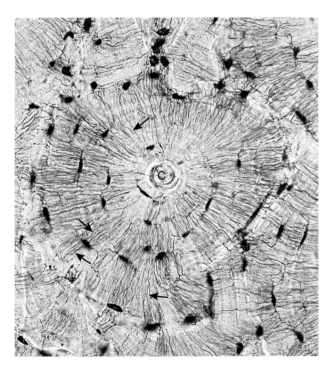

Figure 5-22 *Compact bone* (×270) [C, central (haversian) canal; arrow, canaliculus].

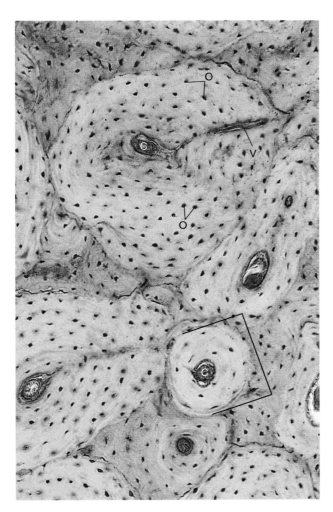

Figure 5-23 *Compact bone* (decalcified, ×162) [V, Volkmann's canal; C, central canal; O, osteocyte; bracket, osteon (haversian system)].

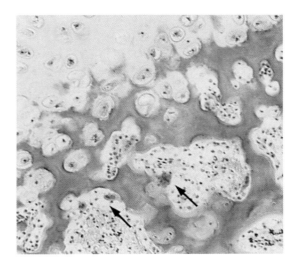

Figure 5-24 *Spongy (cancellous) bone tissue* (high power) [arrows, osteoclasts].

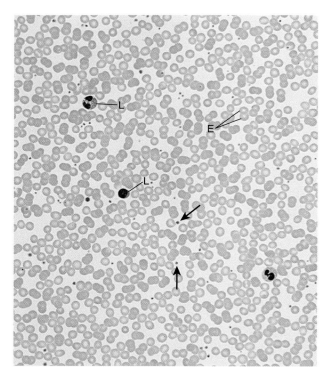

Figure 5-25 *Blood* (smear, ×270) [E, erythrocyte; L, leukocyte; arrow, platelet].

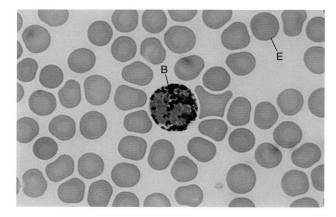

Figure 5-26 *Blood* (smear showing basophil, ×1325) [E, erythrocyte; B, basophil].

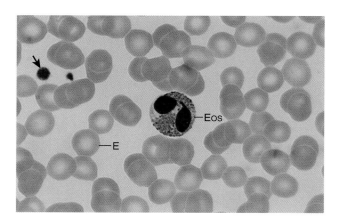

Figure 5-27 *Blood* (smear showing eosinophil, ×1325) [E, erythrocyte; Eos, eosinophil; arrow, platelet].

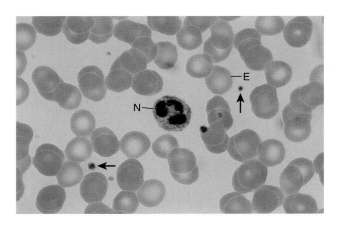

Figure 5-28 *Blood* (smear showing neutrophil, ×1325) [E, erythrocyte; arrow, platelet; N, neutrophil].

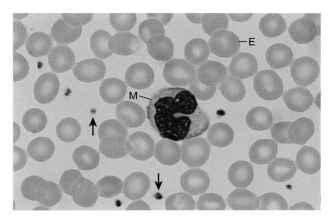

Figure 5-29 *Blood* (smear showing monocyte, ×1325) [E, erythrocyte; M, monocyte; arrow, platelet].

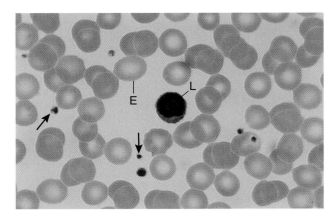

Figure 5-30 *Blood* (smear showing lymphocyte, ×1325) [E, erythrocyte; arrow, platelet; L, lymphocyte].

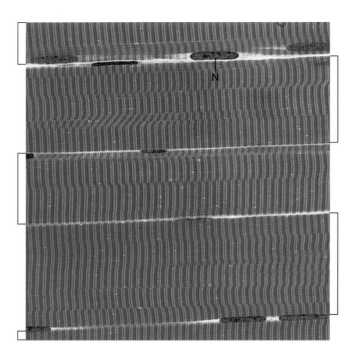

Figure 5-31 *Skeletal muscle* (longitudinal section, ×540) [N, nucleus].

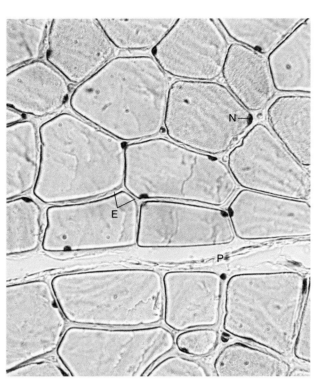

Figure 5-32 *Skeletal muscle* (cross-section, ×540) [E, endomysium; N, nucleus; P, perimysium].

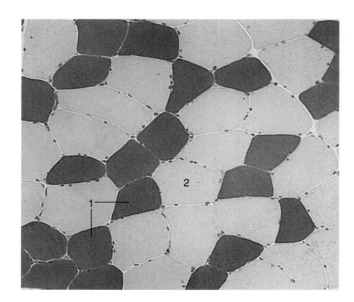

Figure 5-33 *Skeletal muscle* (cross section) [1, type 1 fibers; 2, type 2 fibers].

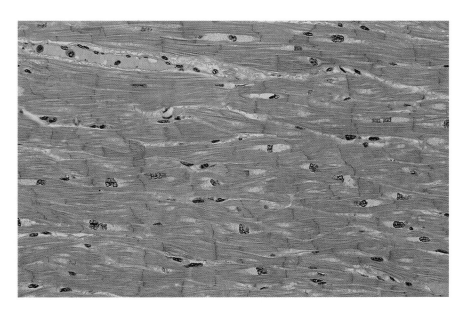

Figure 5-34 *Cardiac muscle showing branching* (longitudinal section, ×270).

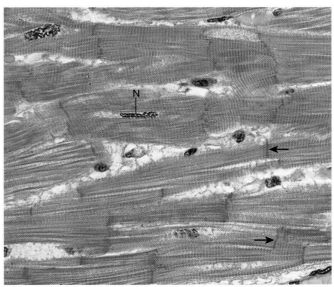

Figure 5-35 *Cardiac muscle* (longitudinal section, ×540) [N, nucleus; arrow, intercalated disk].

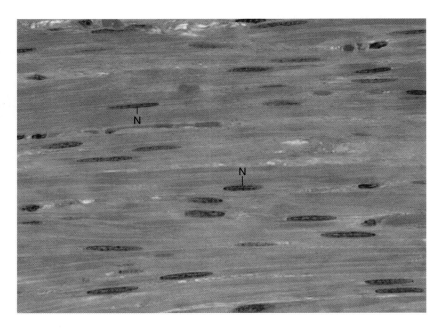

Figure 5-36 *Smooth muscle* (longitudinal section, ×540) [N, nucleus].

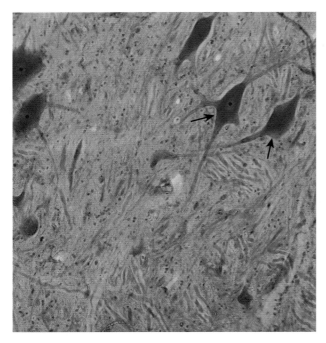

Figure 5-37 *Nerve tissue* (spinal cord gray matter, ×270) [arrow, neuron].

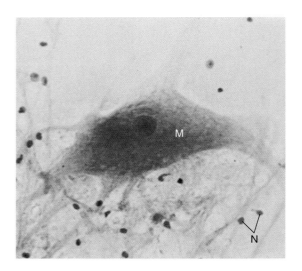

Figure 5-38 *Nerve tissue* (spinal cord smear) [M, multipolar neuron; N, nucleus of glial cell].

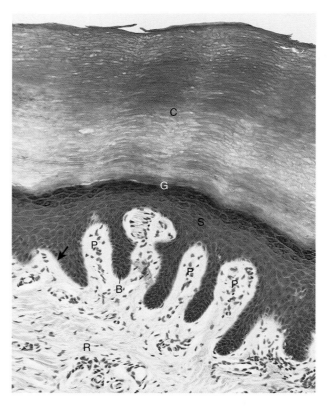

Figure 5-39 *Skin* (thick, ×132) [*Epidermis:* C, stratum corneum; G, stratum granulosom; S, stratum spinosum; B, stratum basale; arrow, dermal-epidermal junction; *Dermis:* P, papilla (papillary region); R, reticular region].

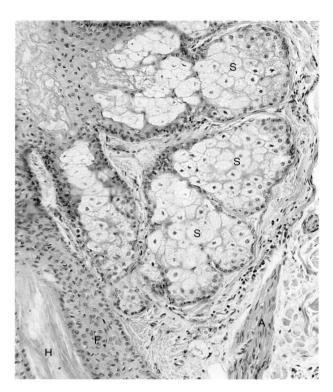

Figure 5-40 *Sebaceous gland* (×132) [S, sebaceous gland; A, arrector pili muscle; H, hair; F, hair follicle].

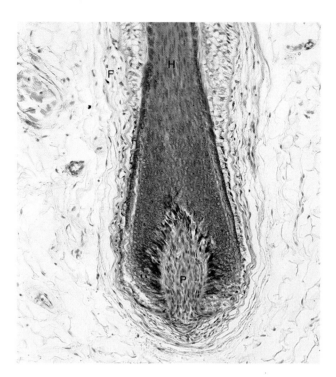

Figure 5-41 *Hair follicle* (longitudinal section, ×132) [F, follicle; H, hair; P, hair papilla].

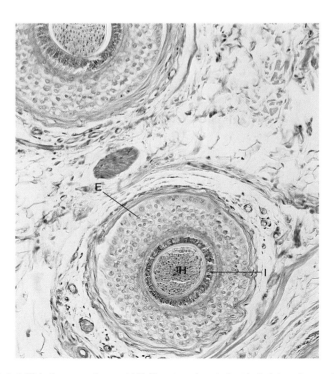

Figure 5-42 *Hair follicle* (cross section, ×132) [E, external root sheath; I, internal root sheath; H, hair].

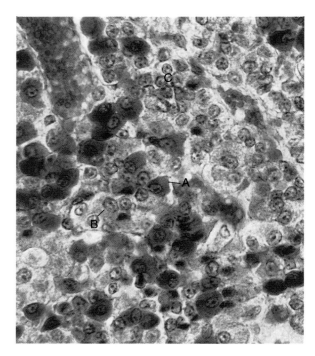

Figure 5-43 *Pituitary gland* (anterior, ×470) [A, acidophil; B, basophil; C, chromophil].

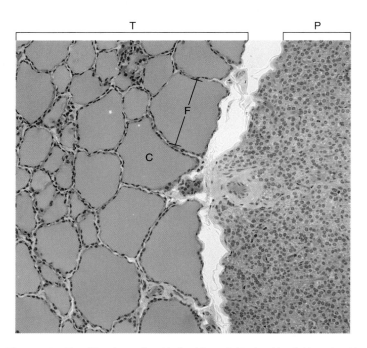

Figure 5-44 *Thyroid and parathyroid gland* (×132) [C, thyroid colloid; F, thyroid follicle; P, parathyroid gland; T, thyroid gland].

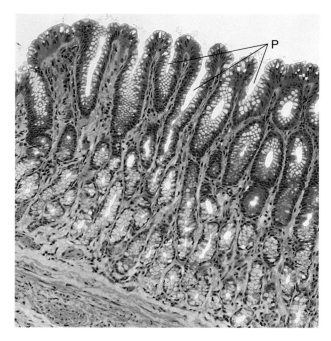

Figure 5-45 Stomach lining (pylorus, ×132) [P, gastric pits].

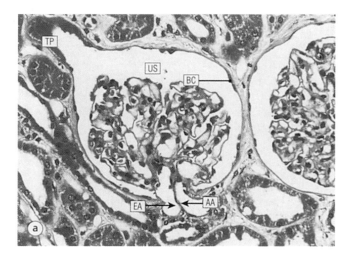

Figure 5-46 Renal corpuscle of kidney [AA, afferent arteriole; EA, efferent arteriole; TP, proximal tubule; US, urinary space of Bowman's capsule; BC, parietal wall of Bowman's capsule].

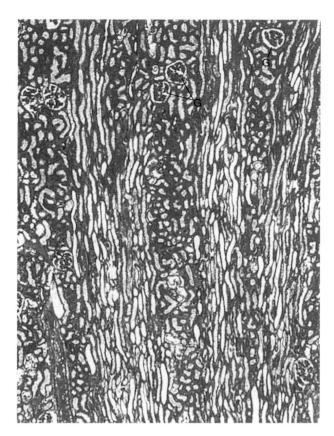

Figure 5-47 *Kidney tubules and blood vessels* [G, glomerulus].

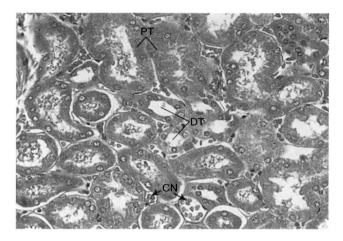

Figure 5-48 *Kidney tubules* (cross section) [PT, proximal tubule; DT, distal tubule; CN, capillary network].

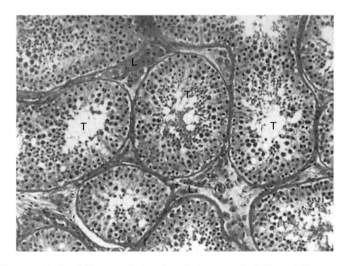

Figure 5-49 *Seminiferous tubules of testis* (cross section) [T, seminiferous tubule; L, interstitial (Leydig) cells].

Figure 5-50 *Ovary* (cross section) [H, hilum; C, cortex; M, medulla].

Photo/Illustration Credits

Part 1

1-1, 1-2, 1-3, 1-4, 1-5, 1-6, 1-7, 1-8, 1-9, 1-10, 1-11, 1-12, 1-13, 1-14, 1-15, 1-16, 1-17, 1-18, 1-19, 1-20, Moses: *Atlas of Clinical Gross Anatomy*, 2005, Elsevier.

Part 2

2-1, 2-2, 2-3, 2-4, 2-6, 2-7, 2-8, 2-9, 2-10, 2-11, D Abrahams: *McMinn's Color Atlas of Human Anatomy*, 5e, 2003, Elsevier.

Part 3

3-1–3-22, D Abrahams: *McMinn's Color Atlas of Human Anatomy*, 5e, 2003, Elsevier.

Part 4

4-1–4-8, D Abrahams: *McMinn's Color Atlas of Human Anatomy*, 5e, 2003, Elsevier; 4-9–4-16, Gosling: *Human Anatomy Color Atlas and Text*, 4e, 2002, Elsevier; 4-17–4-24, Moses: *Atlas of Clinical Gross Anatomy*, 2005, Elsevier.

Part 5

5-1, 5-2, From Pollard & Earnshaw: *Cell Biology*, 2004, Elsevier; 5-3, 5-4, 5-5, 5-6, 5-7, 5-8, 5-9, 5-10, 5-11, 5-12, 5-13, 5-19, 5-20, 5-21, 5-22, 5-23, 5-25, 5-26, 5-27, 5-28, 5-29, 5-30, 5-31, 5-32, 5-34, 5-35, 5-36, 5-37, 5-39, 5-40, 5-41, 5-42, 5-43, 5-44, 5-45, Gartner & Hiatt: *Color Textbook of Histology*, 2e, 2001, Elsevier; 5-14, 5-15, 5-24, 5-38, Leeson, Leeson & Paparo: *Text/Atlas of Histology*, 1988, Elsevier; 5-16, 5-17, 5-18, 5-33, 5-46, 5-47, 5-48, 5-49, 5-50, Stevens & Lowe: *Human Histology*, 3e, 2005, Elsevier.